WITHDRAWN
L. R. COLLEGE LIBRARY

SPORTS
AND
MENTAL HEALTH

SPORTS
AND
MENTAL HEALTH

By

ROBERT A. MOORE, M.D.
Director, Department of Psychiatry
Swedish-American Hospital
Rockford, Illinois
Clinical Assistant Professor of Psychiatry
University of Illinois College of Medicine
Chicago, Illinois

CHARLES C THOMAS • PUBLISHER
Springfield · Illinois · U.S.A.

CARL A. RUDISILL LIBRARY
LENOIR RHYNE COLLEGE

Published and Distributed Throughout the World by
CHARLES C THOMAS • PUBLISHER
BANNERSTONE HOUSE
301-327 East Lawrence Avenue, Springfield, Illinois, U.S.A.
NATCHEZ PLANTATION HOUSE
735 North Atlantic Boulevard, Fort Lauderdale, Florida, U.S.A.

This book is protected by copyright. No
part of it may be reproduced in any manner
without written permission from the publisher.

© *1966, by* CHARLES C THOMAS • PUBLISHER
Library of Congress Catalog Card Number: 66-27442

With THOMAS BOOKS *careful attention is given to all details of
manufacturing and design. It is the Publisher's desire to present books
that are satisfactory as to their physical qualities and artistic possibilities
and appropriate for their particular use.* THOMAS BOOKS *will be true
to those laws of quality that assure a good name and good will.*

796
M78s
81674
Jan. 1973

Printed in the United States of America
H-13

PREFACE

Play and sports, the play of older children and adults, are so much a part of our everyday life we tend to take them for granted. Such activities seem a natural part of life with no need for self-consciousness. Occasionally, brief debates flourish as to the proper place for sports in the school curriculum, usually stimulated by some example of disproportion. In times of national crisis there may develop an attitude that play is too frivolous for such serious times followed shortly by a return of the acceptance of sports as valuable to the morale of the Armed Forces or as a pleasant distraction for the harried people at home.

Oftentimes, the professionals in physical education seem on the defensive with their fellow teachers in the academic fields as if they were unsure if their contributions were as necessary or were just for the promotion of "play." They had already experienced as physical education majors in college the attitude of fellow students which was a mixture of disdain and grudging admiration.

Yet, play and sports seem as old as the history of men and there is little likelihood they will terminate before the termination of man himself. An institution so old, so universal, must be more than frivolous. In fact, we must assume such longevity and universality implies a vital function in play and sports that relates to the survival and stability of social groups.

In the book that follows, we will review the history of sport as we know it, surprised a bit at how much sports have been taken for granted and thus not recorded as a phenomenon of significance. Only in the past few generations has enough interest developed to construct theories about the value of play and sports and we will review these theories.

As the author, I claim the privilege of my own viewpoint (call it prejudice if you must) from this stage on. With my experience as a practicing psychiatrist, with a background in psychoanalysis, I am firmly of the opinion that the psychoanalytic frame of reference makes more facets of human behavior understandable than other theoretic concepts. Thus, I will proceed, with no apologies or attempts at including other explanations, to discuss human nature, its development, and the evolution of play forms.

To consider play and sports as significant only to the individual would be to miss what may be their greatest value—that is, their function as institutions of control which help maintain social living. People constantly rubbing elbows with their neighbors need social lubricants and sports may be one such lubricant.

Recent years have seen an increase in formal application of play and sports as a treatment modality for the chronically ill—especially the mentally ill. No longer considered as mere distraction, a new discipline of recreational therapy has emerged. Attempts are now made to individualize the application of recreational therapy with major utilization of psychodynamic concepts of human behavior and needs.

We will conclude with a discussion of the other side of the issue—the misuse of sports. Unfortunately, anything of value has its overenthusiastic proponents: "With such friends, who needs enemies!" Too often these exaggerations have been confused with the real thing and have stimulated criticism and equally exaggerated counter-positions.

By now, my theme is exposed—I am enthusiastically in favor of play and sports, in their proper proportion, and I will attempt to make a rational case for them.

R.A.M.

CONTENTS

SPORTS
AND
MENTAL HEALTH

Chapter I

A BRIEF HISTORY OF SPORTS

Life must be lived as play, playing certain games, making sacrifices, singing and dancing, and then a man will be able to propitiate the Gods, and defend himself against his enemies, and win in the contest.—PLATO

A HISTORY OF SPORTS as an element in life must be as long as the history of man. If by sports we are talking of the attitude of play, we need not limit ourselves to the history of man. As I write these words, our family's four-month-old beagle puppy is engaged in ferocious battle with an old shoe. Is this merely a consciousless activity as real to him as actual battle? I think not as I see the merry twinkle in his eyes.

To "play" a "game," to engage in a "contest," just to "play," to be "sporting"—all these ideas carry the elements of activity, tension, release of impulses, and joy. "Game" and "contest" further imply order, rules, rhythm, and discipline. Since it is "only a game," it is all in fun and make-believe, and the serious business of living will continue afterwards largely unchanged.

Already we note a looseness of usage requiring an effort at definition. "Play" is the inclusive term that encompasses "games," "contest," and "sports." Webster lists many meanings which include, "to move swiftly, erratically, or intermittently"; "to engage in sport or lively recreation; to amuse or divert oneself; frolic"; "to contend, or take part, in a game"; "to do or execute especially for amusement, profit or education"; and a number of others.

For "game" we find, "sport of any kind; fun"; "an amusement or diversion"; "a contest, physical or mental," according to set rules, undertaken for amusement or for stake."

[3]

"Contest" is defined as an "earnest struggle for superiority, victory, defense, etc.; competition; strife or argument"; and so on.

We discover that "sport" is, "that which diverts, and makes mirth; pastime; diversion"; "a diversion of the field, as hunting, fishing, riding, games, especially athletic games," etc.

For our consideration from this point we will consider these terms in a more constricted sense. A "contest" occurs between two or more opponents, each seeking to outdo the other, but without active intervention in the performance of each other. An example would be a contest in throwing the javelin. A "game" is also between two or more opponents seeking to outdo the other where active intervention in the opponent's activities does occur. Football is obviously a "game," not a contest, but so also is tennis. Both a "game" and a "contest" have rules, limits to the field of activity, and usually time or point limits; in other words, there is a strong element of control and discipline. "Play," on the other hand, is casual, without discipline, and noncompetitive. Swimming, hiking, hunting, and fishing would be examples. "Sports" is the all-inclusive term which covers "games," "contests," and "play" for our use, though as we saw in the more formal definitions "play" could be used as inclusive of "sports."

From the "beginning" we can assume a play attitude existed, since our modern dog possesses it and man had at least his capacity from the onset. Not all hunting was to find food; not all fighting to preserve life. Playing at hunting and fighting not only prepared man for the real thing but it also provided him with a pleasurable experience that made life more bearable. That all activities of primitive man were not utilitarian is shown by the art work to be seen today in numerous caves and rock formations. Unfortunately we lack an adequate chronicle of those days.

While it is not definite at what point play began to be

recorded in history, ancient Egyptian paintings at Beni-Hassan show young women playing catch with a ball. These paintings go back to 2500 B.C. Greek mythology attributes the invention of ball games to the Homeric princess Nausicaa which involved games of catch between maidens. Athletic contests are recorded by Homer as part of the funeral ceremonies given by Achilles for Patroclus. And we must not ignore the way Alexander celebrated the death of Kalanos. A great series of gymnastic, musical, and drinking contests were held. We are not certain of the effects of the first two types of contests but thirty-five of the drinking contestants died on the spot and six a bit later including the hapless victor.

Five basic attitudes towards play and sports through history have been suggested. The earliest is the practical or *military attitude*. This would probably have been the attitude during preliterate society where play was a preparation for hunting and making war. This was certainly the Spartan idea—to prepare the men to be warriors for the State and women to bear more potential warriors. The Romans viewed play similarly, adding a bit more cruelty and blood-letting, and encouraging the spread of the acceptance of war-like violence through large numbers of spectators. In fact, the sports arena, or coliseum, was ordinarily the most prominent building in a city.

This *military attitude* resulted in the beginning of the Olympic games in 776 B.C. Contests were held between the Eleans and the Spartans, even during war-time when a "truce of the gods" was called. The first Olympic consisted of a 200 yard foot-race won by Coroebus, an Elean cook, and his prize was a laurel wreath. The Eleans dominated the races for many years till the Spartans introduced the pentathlon in the eighteenth Olympiad which included the broad jump, javelin throw, foot race, and discus throw. The two best athletes settled the contest with a wrestling match.

Boxing was added in the twenty-third game and four-horse chariot racing in the twenty-fifth. Certainly the military influence is very apparent.

Gradually, however, another attitude, the *art attitude* began to influence sports. The ideas of the Athenians by the fifth century B.C. led to alterations in the Olympics which now began to include sculpture, art, and music—all considered as forms of athletics at that time. The seventy-seventh Olympiad included the whole Mediterranean world and included religious ceremonies. The Athenian ideal was to train as much the mind and esthetic senses as the body. It was stated by Plato: "The mere athlete becomes too much of a savage, and the mere musician is melted and softened beyond what is good for him—the two should therefore be blended in right proportions."

The training of the competitors lasted for ten months. The athlete led a life of abstinence from wine and ate at a training table, his diet consisting of cheese, figs, and wheat bread. Competition was in the nude with bodies covered with olive oil, and thirty-five was the upper age limit. Women were not allowed to participate or even watch under penalty of being dashed to their death off a cliff.

Speaking of women, their desire for sports was not completely stifled. They had their own Olympic games consisting of foot races, called Heraea after the wife and sister of Zeus. Spartan women trained in wrestling, boxing and racing. A sweet Greek enchantress, Atalanta, challenged her suitors to a foot-race and stabbed them in the back till Milanion dropped some golden apples to slow her down. In Jerusalem, women as well as men raced two miles around the Hippodrome.

The ancient Olympics finally were abolished in A.D. 394 by the Emperor Theodosius, the last recorded victor being Varastad, an Armenian.

The *religious attitude* began to develop during that frightening period known as the Dark Ages. Life was so precarious due to marauding heathens and pestilence, that a general denial of the values and pleasures of the body ensued. The life after death became of greater importance and preoccupation with sin and the disciples of the devil was uppermost in most people's minds. Wastefulness was sinful and play was wastefulness. Pleasure was allowed only in religious excesses and this continued through the Medieval and Renaissance periods.

The *religious attitude* has not disappeared to this day and has been an important influence in our lives. To play is to be frivolous. Though the culture no longer says this is so, it is still so to many individuals who find themselves uneasy, even guilty, when they waste time playing. These are the individuals comfortable as long as they work obsessively but moody and irritable on weekends and likely to cut their vacations short to return to work ahead of schedule.

There was a partial return to the *military attitude* during the Medieval period. During the Age of Chivalry, the high-born were expected to excel at arms, and contests of arms were a major source of recreation. Hunting, falconry, archery, swordmanship, horsemanship, etc., were the most vital things for a young man to learn. The warrior class developed a strict code of conduct, codes of chivalry, loyalty, and courtly behavior. This was especially true in England and had much to do with the course of English (later American) history. It was never necessary to maintain a large standing army since all the sons of the nobility and well-to-do formed a ready pool of knights whenever needed. Each local prince or duke was also allowed to keep a specified number of men under arms and was responsible for their training and keep. In fact, his taxes were partly determined by the size of his "army." The lack of a standing military power thus kept the central government from ever wielding the control over the country that was true in most of the rest of Europe.

Gradually, however, there was a loosening of the religious

attitude and people's natural zest for living led to many local sports forms. These games were hardly like those of today but were rather disorganized mayhem between the young men of neighboring villages who would battle for bridges or rough trophies. The day after Lent, Shrove Tuesday, was an especially favored time for such battles. In Scone, Scotland, there was the annual game between the bachelors and the married men—the object being for the married men to get a ball into a small hole and the bachelors to get the ball into the river. On the same day in Inverness, Scotland, a similar battle was held between married and single women. At the other extreme, such a controlled game as cricket was already popular in the 1600's.

Apparently Merry Old England was getting more fun out of life about the time of the first migration to America. Theater was popular, though often illegal, the actors being counted with cattle in the census rather than with people. Lawn bowling, soccer, and field hockey were appearing in rudimentary form, the later two having their antecedents in the intervillage mayhem of an earlier time. Bull-baiting and bear-baiting were popular among the less inhibited, and what could be a better spectator sport than watching the frequent public executions.

By the nineteenth century, organized sports were gaining rapidly in popularity in England, especially the intervillage rivalries. The absence of obligatory military training may have contributed considerably to the interest in sports because of its functions in achieving group loyalty and releasing impulses. As a result, England is considered the cradle of modern sporting life. The ideal was amateurism, playing for the sheer fun of it, and good sportsmanship was as desired as victory itself. In 1840, Thomas Arnold, the headmaster, introduced team sports into the school curriculum at Rugby because of their moral value. The impeccable manners of the athlete in golf and cricket, even in tennis, are the heritage from English amateurism. The "kill the umpire" and win-at-any cost attitudes are the result of increasing professionalism that peculiarly mark American sports. Unfortunately, the same is true elsewhere now as professionalism has become world-wide.

The nineteenth century saw a shift to the *scientific attitude* toward sports. Games were not sinful but neither were they meant entirely for fun. With the rapid growth of medical knowledge of nutrition and public health, and the rapid growth of communication so that the general public could be concerned, the use of sports for health's sake now became prominent. The "play movement" had its rise along with the free school movement, public health movement, and labor movement. Another factor in the nineteenth century emphasizing the need to find a value for sports was the increasingly serious view of life that came with urbanization and industrialization. A period that worried about Realism, Naturalism, Impressionism, and Marxism took itself rather seriously and lost its zest just to be alive. The open fields and streams and playfields were further away. Even clothing styles, especially for men, took on a more serious and less playful appearance.

A natural form to sports that developed from these forces was gymnastics, begun early in the nineteenth century by the Prussian F. L. Jahn. His Turnhalle gymnasium gave rise to the Turnvereine movement throughout Germany. Somewhat earlier than this was the Philanthropinium founded in Dessau by Basedow in 1774 where were taught riding, fencing, vaulting, carpentry, running, and wrestling - rather reminiscient of the old Olympics. In Sweden, Peter Ling organized the Royal Central Institute of Gymnastics in 1814 where teachers were trained for the Army. The Gymnastic Institute in Copenhagen was started in 1804 for Army officers. Gymnastics even today holds wide appeal in Scandinavian countries. The Swedish influence was very strong in the French schools by the 1890's, earlier having an influence only on the Army. From this we see a recurrence of the *military attitude* now fused with the *scientific*.

Let us back up a bit to get a picture of the attitudes toward play and sports in the United States. As we recall there was a loosening of the old *religious attitude* in England at the time of the migration. Unfortunately, the rigors of life in the New World were so great there was little room for fun in the beginning. We forget what a large proportion of the earliest settlers died within the first year or so because of their gross ignorance of survival techniques in the wilderness and their insistence in "doing like in England" in a place that bore little resemblance to England. For many generations it was the unusual family that had not lost small children or even a wife or two.

In addition, the *religious attitude* was exported to America and stimulated there by the facts of life that made the soul a somewhat more stable possession than the body. Religion was a potent force in early America though its formal influence decreased as one left the larger communities. Nevertheless, the idea that every activity had to be utilitarian held wide sway and for obvious practical reasons. It is not hard to see how the American attitude of the virtues of hard work, "getting ahead," and down-grading of the "frills" got its origin.

What play was allowed was either associated with work or church. A camp meeting, thrashing or house-raising was a break in the monotony of life and brought people together from scattered farms and settlements. News was exchanged, old friends visited, and a little fun allowed to sneak in. Laws in the early colonies actually forbad too obvious play.

People being people, however, we can assume that play occurred, perhaps in preparation for hunting and self-defense, competition in farming and woodsman skills, shooting matches, wrestling, and even such frivolity as pitching horse-shoes. Apparently the southern colonies were more casual and allowed fox hunts and horse races.

As the population grew and migration continued westward, the "sports" of the day moved westward too. Hunting and log-rolling moved out with the frontier. The developing cities grew so rapidly they did not provide the parks and other facilities more typical of European cities that had had time to mellow. Instead, with an endless abundance of land, the cities were rows of houses, one on top of the other. This lack of room for play was a major factor in the later development of "spectatoritis" since it takes much less room for a lot of people to watch one baseball game than for them all to play in a number of baseball games.

To return to our main stream of development, at the same time the *scientific attitude,* mixed with vestiges of the *military,* was in the ascendancy, there was also a diminution of the *religious attitude.* Thus, we see in the nineteenth century a parallel movement of sports for the good of it and sports for the fun of it. England was the great exporter of sports for the fun of it to Europe and the United States while Germany and the Scandinavian countries were exporting sports for the good of it. Golf, tennis, badminton, rowing and soccer got their impetus from England and were carried to the colonial worlds like the stiff upper lip, gin (actually a Dutch invention), and pounds Sterling. Athletic clubs became the style in the nineteenth century—the first being the Royal Military Academy in England established in 1849. Originally organized for social standing as well as recreation, the American twist was to try and win. As a result, young men with more muscles than blue blood were added to the club rosters and professionalism had its birth. It is of interest to note that the present major league baseball and football teams are officially called "clubs."

Team sports and organized competition had a special appeal in the United States and with this a great increase in spectator appeal. Horse racing was the original spectator sport but baseball followed close behind. Admission was charged to baseball games as early as 1858.

Probably the Civil War was a major factor in increasing interest in team games, both to play and watch. For the first time, men from all walks of life and all corners of the country were brought together and learned what each other was doing. Recreation was a major problem for the soldiers and impromptu baseball games became immensely popular. Naturally, when the veteran, Blue or Gray, returned home baseball went with him. Other sports were taken home too and football became a part of the American scene with the first intercollegiate game taking place between Princeton and Rutgers in 1869. With the great increase in interest and need for control, the Amateur Athletic Union was established in 1888 and has remained a potent force in amateur sports to this day.

In 1896 occurred the revival of the Olympic games. The modern Olympics were organized under the stimulation of Pierre de Coubertin of France. Rather than a special interest in sports itself, the major motivation seems to have been based on the belief that sports excellence in English schools had been a major influence in England's long position as a world leader. The first modern Olympiad was held in Athens with no age limit as had been true previously. Although women were not immediately included they were in 1912. The first winter version of the Olympics were held in Chamonix, France, in 1924.

The "play movement" with its origins in the *scientific attitude* in Europe began to have its effects in the United States in the late nineteenth century. Partly this was a result of the migration of Germans and Swedes with their gymnastic interests. Probably more importantly it was a result of an idea jumping the ocean. The first unsupervised recreational facility was Washington Park in Chicago, dating from 1876; the first organized camp for boys was started in New Hampshire in 1880. The first organized playgrounds with recreation leaders were established in Boston in 1886 but had spread to only ten cities by 1900. A pioneer movement of great impact was the beginning of the Hull House playground by Jane Addams in Chicago in 1894. Because of its cramped quarters and the need for new recreational outlets, such sports as softball, volleyball, and outdoor basketball received a major stimulus here. In 1903, the first public school athletic league was established in New York City; the Playground and Recreational Association of America began in 1906 and eventually became the National Recreational Association; in 1910 the Boy Scouts were started, the Camp Fire Girls, and Girl Scouts in 1912. Intramural sports were introduced into colleges in 1915 and into high schools in 1925.

A similar growth of the "play movement" occurred in other parts of the world as the idea was carried across international boundaries with ease. Turkey was strongly influenced by the Swedish gymnastics; Japan by the YMCA; India and Pakistan by the English model of field hockey, cricket, and soccer; Latin American also by the YMCA.

However, it remained again for wars to spread ideas as was true of the Civil War in the U. S. World War I brought millions into contact with both team sports and gymnastics. The large numbers of physically unfit young men discovered in the induction shocked the educational world with the result there was a major increase in physical education. World War II had a similar effect, especially on Russia. Before the war there had been little development of the "play movement" but after a major effort was made to catch up with and surpass the rest of Europe and the U. S. The All-Union Committee of Physical Culture had the responsibility of coordinating gymnastics and sports for both school students and working people. Sports clubs were established and supported by the government and labor unions. It is estimated that 20 per cent of the resources of labor unions and 50 per cent of the educational budget were invested in sports and a mass program of physical fitness. Team sports gained increasing public interest, especially soccer, but also basketball and volleyball. Even China felt the impact. Previously, for 4000 years, it was felt that gentlemen and scholars did not exercise but now a national fitness program developed.

Gradually a more liberal view of sports has emerged, the *social attitude*. The *military* and *scientific attitudes* have receded though not disappeared and they have a tendency to increase during times of national emergency. The *social attitude* assumes that sports are an opportunity to learn about living competitively with others and in alliance with others through teams. Life is a game. In totalitarian countries this change is less noticeable since sports have been a major tool with which to mold a population into a militaristic frame of mind as exemplified in Nazi Germany.

While this shift has been particularly great in the U. S. where the *scientific* and *military attitudes* never were so strong, it has also occurred in countries like Sweden where they have been strong. The truth is the youth of the U. S. have never been able to get too excited about "exercises" and gymnastics but rather have relished fun and direct competition.

Let us turn now to a consideration of sports with a social orientation in the U. S. We have noted the great impetus given to sports by the Civil War, especially to baseball, and to a lesser degree to football. Since both baseball and football have antecedents in English play, we must satisfy our chauvinism with basketball, invented in 1891 by James A. Naismith.

Baseball gained very rapid popularity after the Civil War. Every village and neighborhood had its team and "sand-lot" pickup games became the favorite pass-time of the mass of American boys. The increasing pressure of the better players and the number of spectators led to the development of professional teams. With increasing methods of communication the "star" system began to form with the sports hero being known from one end of the country to another—a model for the adolescent boy to emulate.

Basketball and football remained amateur sports for many years—especially at the high school and college levels. Baseball had a big head-start in the public eye and retained its prominence as the National Pastime for generations. Other competitive sports more individually-oriented did not seem to catch the fancy of American sports fans. The interest was in *the team*—a group with which both the player and the spectator could identify. Joy and despair could seize an entire town or school-body as its team's fortunes varied, as per the "Mighty Casey at the Bat."

In keeping with human nature, the identification with *the team* began to replace other more significant activities. In schools, sports reached a prominence superior to scholarship, especially in smaller communities. The football or basketball team and its coach became more important than the physics or English teachers, than the principal, and even the better judgment of the school board under pressure from the public. The athlete became relatively untouchable in such matters as discipline and studies; even worse, he was encouraged to develop an unrealistic picture of himself. He discovered that his varsity letter did not assure him a successful future unless he was the unusually good performer. The high-school basketball star caught up in the frenzy of the state championship tournaments in such states as Indiana and Illinois might face the sad fact the greatest day in his life had already been experienced while still a teenager.

The past few years have seen significant changes occurring on the American sports scene, though still the emphasis has remained very much within the *social attitude*. In professional sports we are witnessing the relative decline in baseball— while the attendance records go up, the piece of the spec-

tator dollar is declining. Professional football is now in the
ascendance, formed by tremendous television exposure. The
raw aggression of the game has caught a part of the
unconscious world of the spectator that has never been
touched by baseball. College football has had to compete with
professional football. The result has been increasing diffi-
culty for the small school or the college that treats football
as an amateur sport. The big colleges have kept their
fans by a semi-professionalism that has reached rather cynical
proportions though controls by the National Collegiate Athletic Association have corrected this to a considerable degree
in recent years.

It is interesting to note how little effect migration has
had on team sports in America. While basketball is the
only pure native sport, the form baseball and football have
taken make them also peculiarly American. No one really
challenges our right to stage the World Series or World
Championship games in professional basketball and football.
Despite massive migrations from European countries where
soccer was endemic, there has never developed a large interest in this most exciting sport. The only significant exception is ice hockey which has filtered down from Canada,
though its effects have been limited, largely, to the North
Central and North Eastern States. In fact, we notice that
almost the entire personnel of the National Hockey League
clubs are Canadian. Even the top college hockey teams have
been manned by Canadians.

Actually, this lack of change in the sports scene is simply
part of a bigger picture. While we talk of a "melting pot,"
George Steward, in *American Ways of Life,* has shown that
the picture has been more one of assimilation. The basic
picture of American life was established by the early citizens
as soundly Anglo-Saxon, and each wave of migrants, after
a brief struggle to maintain its integrity, has quickly taken on
the larger cultural colorations. Not that certain language

and food habits don't reveal certain European influences, but the net effect has been negligible.

We are now witnessing an interesting contradiction in team sports. The college and professional teams emphasize sports for the elite and create great spectator interest. At the same time there has been an increasing awareness of the need for team sports for the average participant. This is exemplified in the development of intramural teams, compulsory physical education classes, church and city recreational leagues, industrial leagues, etc. For the younger boys, Little League and similar organizations have provided an opportunity for all but the most awkward or disinterested to play. We will speak later of some abuses that have crept in here, however.

It is in the area of individual sports, however, where the greatest spurt has occurred since World War II. Previously, golf, tennis, and skiing, as examples, were enjoyed by members of private clubs and the wealthy. This was especially true of skiing because of the need for expensive travel. This has changed considerably with the rapid expansion of municipal golf courses and tennis courts. Many housing developments now advertise their lots with emphasis on a neighborhood golf course. The explosion in numbers who ski is particularly remarkable. So hungry are the ski enthusiasts that they don't even demand much in the way of hills. Michigan, without more than a ripple in its geography, heads the nation in ski centers. So as not to lose an opportunity to use the ridges, lights are used at night and snowmakers where there is inadequate snow. Whether or not there is any truth to the allegation that stretch pants gave skiing its present populariy depends on one's view.

Another phenomenon has been the growth of bowling, especially league bowling. These leagues are often oriented to industry and to accommodate the different work shifts the bowling is in shifts—practically full utilization of the alleys.

Hunting and fishing have benefited from the greater ease of transportation. The new super-highways speed the outdoorsman in a space of three or four hours from the city to the woods and streams. Unfortunately, over-utilization has depleted the bag making it easier to get there and back empty-handed.

The awareness of the health-preservative aspects of regular exercise has given a new emphasis to squash, hand-ball, and swimming. True to the American view of things, the exercises have to be fun to be popular.

This increased emphasis on individual sports has resulted in remarkable changes in world record times and distances. From the late nineteenth century to the present, changes have been from almost thirty minutes for the 1500 meters swim to seventeen minutes; 10.3 seconds for the 100 yard dash to 9.1; four and a half minutes for the mile run to the frequent sub-four minute mile; forty-three feet for the shotput to nearly seventy feet, etc. By the 1952 and 1956 Olympics, the women were surpassing the men's records for 1896 *even when they were menstruating.* Unfortunately the Olympics have been marred in recent years by a switch of emphasis from individual performance to team performance. The Cold War has pitted the huge Russian and U. S. contigents against each other and the smaller countries seem to have been squeezed out. This is largely an illusion however. In the 1952 Helsinki games, for example, the U. S. A. and U. S. S. R., with 346,000,000 population got 17,706 points; the four Scandinavian countries with 19,000,000 population got 12,873 points—a ratio of over ten to one in favor of these small countries.

While we have been reviewing this sweep of change in the form of sports participation, what has happened to those groups largely by-passed by civilization? As might be expected they still play games much as their ancestors. While they are familiar with modern sports, they have not lost their old ones. Among the New Zealand Maoris, games have a serious and war-like character but with elaborate rules of honor. There seems to be great enjoyment because of a lack of puritanical religious influence. Fathers spend much time training their sons in hunting, fishing, war dances, the use of weapons, and hand-to-hand combat. Competitions between villages include wrestling, weapons contests, canoe races, posture dances and dart throwing. A special favorite is throwing spears at each other from a distance of fifty feet. The Fijians also enjoy village contests of foot races, tug-of-war, leap frog, etc.

In summary, man has played throughout his history. The attitudes, however, have changed through the years through those classified as military, art, religious, scientific, and social. The latter is true of today and emphasizes the pleasures and social advantages of sports.

REFERENCES

1. Huizenga, Johan: *Homo Ludens: A Study of the Play-Element in Culture.* New York, Roy Publishers, 1950.
2. Jokl, Ernst: The athletic status of women. *British Journal of Physical Medicine, 20:*247-253, 1957.
3. Jokl, E., Karvonen, M. J., Kihlberg, J., Koskela, A., and Noro, L.: *Sports in the Cultural Pattern of the World.* Helsinki, Institute of Occupational Health, 1956.
4. Ryan, Allan J.: The Olympic Games and the Olympic ideal. *Journal of the American Medical Association, 162:*1105-1109, 1956.
5. Ryde, David: The effects of strenuous exertion on women. *Practitioner, 177:*73-77, 1956.
6. Sapora, Allen V., and Mitchell, Elmer D.: *The Theory of Play and Recreation,* Third Edition. New York, Ronald Press, 1961.
7. Stewart, George R.: *American Ways of Life.* Garden City, Doubleday and Company, Inc., 1954.
8. Stokes, Adrian: Psycho-analytic reflections on the development of ball games, particularly cricket. *International Journal of Psychoanalysis, 37:*185-192, 1956.
9. Stumpf, Florence, and Cozens, Frederick W.: Some aspects of the

role of games, sports, and recreational activities in the culture of modern primitive peoples. I. The New Zealand Maoris. *Research Quarterly, 18*:198-218, 1947. II. The Fijians. *Research Quarterly, 20*:2-20, 1949.

10. Wilson, K. E.: Sports. *Journal of the American Medical Association, 167*:1392-5, 1958.

11. Zimmerman, Helen M.: Physical activity experience and interests of college women. *Research Quarterly, 25*:109-118, 1954.

Chapter II

THEORIES OF PLAY AND SPORTS

Children find in play the medium for satisfaction of the great majority of their motives. Indeed, to children play is the serious business of life.—E. D. MITCHELL AND B. S. MASON

IT MIGHT BE ARGUED that we play just for fun and without any deeper reason than that. However, our present view of human behavior is that nothing we do is purely frivolous but has a purpose behind it. Our actions are valuable to us in that they gratify certain hidden impulses or help us to hide these impulses from ourselves and others.

In this chapter we will review briefly some of the theories presented over the years to account for man's universal need to play. We may feel none of these theories are quite adequate or that they are contrived, as an afterthought, to explain behavior that requires no explanation. We will be particularly interested in the theories of the Dutch philosopher Johan Huizinga but we will also see what other thinkers have made of play and sports. Ultimately, we will consider certain psychoanalytic explanations as most suited to the observable data.

The *surplus energy theory* has long held wide appeal. It holds that energy still unexpended after the necessities of life are satisfied find their expression in play activity. The names of the poet Schiller and the psychologist Spencer are associated with this theory. The child would be most free to play as so little of its energy is required for existence. We will see later this is a gross misunderstanding of the nature of childhood which is a very serious and business-like period. Any observant parent might wonder why a child has so much surplus energy to use in play but so little to use for chores. He might further note how children will continue their play-day far into the night if allowed to, long after this energy is no longer "surplus." They fight manfully against the encroachments of darkness and bed-time till they almost drop in their tracks. The concept that children, animals and insects use play in their expenditure of surplus energy overlooks the important reasons behind the apparent playful activities.

Two psychologists, Groos in 1898 and McDougall in 1918, developed the *instinct theory* to account for play. Groos in particular emphasized man's need to have a prolonged period of practice through play before his native endowments, or instincts, were sufficiently developed to prepare him for life. A child running aimlessly or playing hide-and-seek is not playing for the fun of it but is trying new and more mature ways to express his basic impulses. The lower animal, on the contrary, with its much shorter "childhood" has its instinctual life developed near to the adult level almost from birth. We can see that the *instinct theory* is diametrically opposite from the *surplus energy theory*. In fact, it seems to anticipate the psychoanalytic concepts we will discuss later.

The *recreation theory* was originally postulated by Lord Kames in 1782 and enlarged upon by Patrick, Guts Muth and Lazurus. It also is diametrically opposite to the *surplus energy theory* in that it explains the value of play as a means of re-creating energy or refreshing the person so he can again pursue the more serious responsibilities of life. Many people feel much more invigorated after a vacation spent in active play than one spent in merely resting. This is especially true of the more obsessive and driven character who tends to become bored and even depressed if not active. For him, a week in a beach chair is fatiguing whereas a week of sailing, swimming, and golf leaves him refreshed and full of energy to return to work. Patrick in 1916 modified the *recreation theory* with the *relaxation theory*. He felt that the strains of adult living, especially with the emphasis on intellectual demands, were relieved by regressing to activities common in childhood or in primitive times when the large muscles predominated.

In 1906, Hall proposed the *recapitulation theory* that was based on a now-discarded premise that acquired characteristics could be transmitted to future generations by heredity. As we become more civilized, we have moved from large muscle activity to small muscle and brain activity. When we play we return to older forms of activity which emphasize large muscles and the exuberance that comes from using them. As one grew older his play tendencies reflected the behavior of more recent evolutionary development. Our present biological knowledge makes this theory untenable.

The *catharsis theory* is as old as Aristotle and would seem to be compatible with our more modern psychological concepts. Play is seen as a chance to express certain emotions that would otherwise have to be dammed up because of social pressures. One can engage in combative games without censor and then be under less pressure to be combative in inappropriate cricumstances.

Mitchell and Mason advanced the *self-expression theory* in 1934. In their opinion, man has an inherent wish to express himself, that is his deeper wishes and urges. His methods of expression are determined by his anatomical capacities, his present physical fitness, his habitual inclinations, his social contacts, and his physical environment. [Since much more pleasure is obtained when a skill is mastered, he tends to repeat activities he does well in and drop those in which he doesn't.] The early process of learning a skill only becomes fun as he sees himself obtaining some mastery. If self-expression is blocked he seeks expression through phantasy formation. This may account for the great increase in spectator interest in sports including T. V. If one can't be a plunging fullback at least one can vicariously enjoy watching one plunge. The *self-expression theory* incorporates so much that is obviously true; however, it lacks penetration into the real motivations in play though it tends to be in general agreement with psychoanalytic theory.

We will review in greater detail a most interesting theory by the Dutch historian Johan Huizinga which is referred to as the *genetic theory*. He described his concepts in an intriguing book entitled *Homo Ludens: A Study of the Play-Element in Culture*. The title is translated from Latin as "Man, the Player." Play has a meaning for lower animals as well as man and the essence of play is "fun." Play has six elements that define it: (1) Play is a voluntary activity; (2) play is a stepping out of "real life"; (3) play has limits of time and place; (4) play is repetitive; (5) play demands an order to it; and (6) play involves tension especially when it is competitive. This leads to the definition of play as "—a voluntary activity or occupation executed within certain fixed limits of time and place, according to rules freely accepted but absolutely binding, having its aim in itself and accompanied by a feeling of tension, joy and consciousness that it is 'different' from 'ordinary life.' ")

While certain languages such as Greek, Sanskrit, and Blackfoot Indian have separate words for play and contest, in Latin there is only the one, *ludere*. The result is the common use of one word to stand for contest, battle, rapid movement, hunting, etc. Thus, the higher forms of play have as their objective to win over another or to gain superiority or prestige. In Greek the words "prize" and "athlete" have similar roots.

The development of play forms has evolved through history from the agonistic instinct, that is the human need to fight. "Virtue" has its roots in "virility" and virtue, honor, and glory are the goals of play. We see here the origins of the Olympic Games which started during the agonal period of Greek history and reflect the *military attitude* of sports. "Agonal" also implies suffering and the early contests involved trials of great suffering.

Some historians are cited by Huizinga as suggesting the shift from battle to play leads to decadence in the long run but he disputes this. "Coupled with this play-sense is a spirit that strives for honour, dignity, superiority, and beauty. Magic and mystery, heroic longings, the foreshadowing of music, sculpture and logic all seek form and expression in noble play."

The agonal instinct given play elements is seen in our legal courts. In ancient Greece litigation was a contest to be won rather than an effort to determine right versus wrong. To a degree, this remains true today in the advisory form of justice though it is assumed that if both sides in the contest have their chance, the side that wins is more likely to be the side of right. Among the Greenland Eskimos litigation consists of a drumming contest with festival trimmings. The plaintiff and defendant sing insults to each other and the audience decides who wins, i.e., who is right. If the "rules of justice" are not followed, however, it is no longer play and everyone feels cheated.

The rules of war must also be followed for it to be fun. War is seen as noble and virtuous—purifying the nation and leading it to a higher level of civilization. This concept seems alien at first glance when we consider the suffering inherent in war. Yet, societies seem to flourish from war which unites a people, gives them a sense of common direction, and gives them pride in themselves. A very recent example is the outbreak of hostilities between Pakistan and India over Kashmir. Though the territory was left relatively unchanged, the results seemed beneficial to India. It was a nation split by rivalries, with pressures for secession of certain areas, and feeling its national pride humiliated after losing skirmishes with China two years earlier. The fighting gave a new purpose to the country and an increased sense of belonging to something worthwhile.

The play-element in war, however, is lost when the rules are not followed. Then war becomes barbaric as the original violence becomes manifest; "—in the absence of the play-spirit civilization is impossible." The genocide by Nazi Germany in World War II is an example of this. Here the rules were so badly broken the near total destruction of Germany was necessary as a cleansing operation. Afterwards, a new Germany could emerge with a new sense of pride.

Unfortunately, Huizinga sees a loss of the play-spirit in sports because of professionalism (and now television extravaganza). Play has become a business. On the other hand, perhaps the play-element is preserved in business through the contest of competition. He makes the following rather somber observations of today: "The great competitions in archaic cultures had always formed part of the sacred festivals and were indispensable as health and happiness-bringing activities. This ritual tie has now been completely severed; sport has become profane; 'unholy' in every way and has no organic connection whatever with the structure of society, least of all when prescribed by the government. The ability of modern social techniques to stage mass demonstrations with the maximum of outward show in the field of athletics does not alter the fact that neither the Olympiads nor the organized sports of American universities nor the loudly trumpeted international contests have, in the smallest degree, raised sport to the level of a culture-creating activity. However important it may be for the players or spectators, it remains sterile. The old play-factor has undergone almost complete atrophy."

This view seems to be shared by an anthropologist, Alpenfels, who feels our society has come to separate work and play. Work is serious and important; play is frivolous and wasteful. By contrast, more primitive societies retain more of the play-element in "important" activities. She suggests our schools should counter this change. While educators are quite aware of the value of learning being seen as a game, they may be inhibited by the no-nonsense attitude of the school board and parents, especially since the Sputnik panic of a few years ago. Time spent on teaching how to live happily and creatively merely takes away from time that could be spent on the essential 3 R's. It is rather tragic that our technical knowledge has so far outrun our social knowledge that we face the spector of now being able to exterminate ourselves and not being sure how to prevent it since we have not learned how to live together. As work and production become our ideals and as play becomes less evident, we approach a "cultural bankruptcy."

More recent psychological studies of play activity have emphasized the value of play in learning the essentials of the functioning of one's own body, then the relationship between self and a companion, then between self and the peer group. This gives play the significance of "trying life on for size," preparing for something ahead which is serious and more important. It would appear, then, that play has importance only to the child as it leads him to the day when he is an adult and no longer has need or time for play. Piaget points out the pleasure at mastery the child feels as he repeats patterns of response (schemas) and the additional pleasure experienced by the slight alterations in already learned behavior. Unfortunately the end for the child is to reach a state where he responds to rules and reality and loses the pleasure and excitement that he felt in learning new play forms as a child.

Psychoanalytic literature has not ignored the significance of play and such authors as Phyllis Greenacre, Franz Alexander, Lili Peller, Erik Erickson, Robert Waelder, Adrian Stokes, and Melanie Klein, among others, deserve mention. The psychoanalytic concepts can be summarized under four categories: (1) mastery, (2) impulse outlet, (3) relief from the demands of reality and the superego, and (4) functional pleasure.

The use of play as a means of mastery has been described by Greenacre, Peller, Erickson, and Waelder. A great deal of anxiety is produced in a child who experiences a traumatic situation or who faces an overwhelming stimulation or demand. By reducing the experience to "just play," he can act it out over and over till finally he feels he can handle or master it. A child who has lost a parent may "solve" his loss by creating a family of dolls and other play objects. At first he might deny the loss by emphasizing his interest in the doll that represents the lost parent, then gradually lose interest in this doll and finally banish it from the "family." It is as if he had control over whether the doll (parent) was present or absent, and he could not be surprised by such a loss.

Stokes and Alexander, among others, describe the value of play as a form of outlet for basic drives. Stokes emphasizes the aggressive outlet in play and sees games as a substitute for warfare. Alexander points out play may function as an expression of libidinal (sexual) energy that is in excess of that required for normal living. We recall the earlier description of the *surplus energy theory*.

Waelder observes the value of play as being similar to phantasy or certain creative activity. Since it is "only play" we can rescind the laws of reality and have the world be whatever we wish it to be. Further, we may temporarily even ignore the voice of our conscience and dare ideas and action just because it isn't "real." Such a "regression in the service of the ego" has a definite value in our psychic economy by reducing our energy output required for constant repression. Lantos points out that the return of the super-ego changes play activities back to work activities, that is, we are now doing something "real" and "worthwhile."

Functional pleasure in play has been demonstrated by

Melanie Klein and Waelder. The pure joy of unrestricted physical movement, the freedom of large muscles to stretch to their limits is a luxury once tasted that can be addictive. This pleasure in motion may have a large element of sexual libidinal energy.

We may conclude our discussion of psychoanalytic conceptions of play by quoting Sigmund Freud: "Every playing child behaves like a poet, in that he creates a world of his own, or more accurately expressed, he transposes things into his own world according to a new arrangement which is to his liking. It would be unfair to believe that he does not take this world seriously; on the contrary, he takes his play very seriously, he spends large amounts of affect on it. The antithesis of play is reality, not seriousness. The child differentiates his play world from reality very well, in spite of all the effective cathexis, and gladly lets his imaginary objects and relationships depend upon the tangible and visible things of the real world. Only this dependence differentiates the 'play' of children from 'phantasying.'" Waelder adds, "Fantasy woven about a real object is, however, nothing more than: play."

In summary, we have assumed that play is not just for its own sake but has a serious purpose in human behavior. We have reviewed briefly the following explanations of play: surplus energy theory, instinct theory, recreation theory, relaxation theory, recapitulation theory, catharsis theory, self-expression theory, genetic theory, and psychoanalytic theory. The last named includes four elements: mastery, impulse outlet, relief from the demands of reality and the super-ego, and functional pleasure. We will pursue psychoanalytic theory in much greater detail.

REFERENCES

1. Alexander, Franz: A contribution to the theory of play. *Psychoanalytic Quarterly,* 27:175-193, 1958.
2. Alpenfels, Ethel: Work and play as seen by an anthropologist. *Childhood Education, 25*:149-152, 1948.

3. Deutsch, Helene: A contribution to the psychology of sports. *International Journal of Psychoanalysis, 7*:223-227, 1926.

4. Erickson, Erik H.: *Childhood and Society.* New York, W. W. Norton and Company, Inc., 1950.

5. Freud, Sigmund: The relation of the past to day-dreaming. *Collected Papers,* Volume IV. London, Hogarth Press, 1950.

6. Greenacre, Phyllis: Play in relation to creative imagination. *Psychoanalytic Studies of the Child, 14*:61-80, 1959.

7. Huizenga, Johan: *Homo Ludens: A Study of the Play-Element in Culture.* New York, Roy Publishers, 1950.

8. Klein, Melanie: Infant analysis. *International Journal of Psychoanalysis, 7*:31-63, 1926.

9. Lantos, Barbara: Metapsychological considerations on the concept of work. *International Journal of Psychoanalysis, 33*:439-443, 1952.

10. Layman, Emma McClay: *Mental Health through Physical Education and Recreation.* Minneapolis, Burgess Publishing Company, 1955.

11. Peller, Lili E.: Models of children's play. *Mental Hygiene, N.Y., 36*:66-83, 1952.

12. Peller, Lili E.: Libidinal phases, ego development, and play. *Psychoanalytic Studies of the Child, 9*:178-198, 1954.

13. Peller, Lili E.: Libidinal development as reflected in play. *Psychoanalysis, 3*:3-12, 1955.

14. Philips, Richard H.: The nature and function of children's formal games. *Psychoanalytic Quarterly, 29*:200-207, 1960.

15. P. M. T.: Bread and Circuses. *Mental Health, London, 8*:95-99, 1949.

16. Sapora, Allen V., and Mitchell, Elmer D.: *The Theory of Play and Recreation,* Third Edition. New York, Ronald Press, 1961.

17. Waelder, Robert: The psychoanalytic theory of play. *Psychoanalytic Quarterly, 2*:208-224, 1933.

18. White, Robert W.: Motivation reconsidered: the concept of competence. *Psychological Review, 66*:297-333, 1959.

Chapter III

PSYCHOLOGICAL DEVELOPMENT
AND HUMAN NATURE

BEFORE WE consider the meaning of play and sports at various ages, it will be necessary to review the deeper elements in human development and behavior. For the psychologically trained, this chapter is a review of already well-known conceptualizations and valuable time would be preserved by passing it by. For the person who is aware of present-day views of human nature, it may seem also but a review, but I would encourage you to accompany me through this exercise so we are speaking the same language; you will not be surprised by what you find. For the person who lives in that comfortable world where all is as it seems on the surface, this may seem unjustified and perhaps pathological speculation unworthy of further consideration. However, please come along so that all that follows in later chapters has some significance.

For most of the history of speculation about human nature, there has existed a peculiar paradox. On the one hand we have believed that children are born pure of heart, live through an ecstatic period known as the "happy years of childhood," then are gradually eroded by the pain and complexities of adult existence. Early suggestions by Freud that children harbored certain impulsive wishes were met by derision from the highest medical authorities. In contrast, up till the nineteenth century, children were held responsible for crimes as if they had the same reasoning and control as adults. Children below ten were hung for stealing food and objects of little value. A child was seen as an adult in miniature.

[31]

We will review the concepts of psychological development and human nature from the psychoanalytic frame of reference without apology and without any attempt at being "eclectic." Other systems of explanation will be ignored, not because they lack value, but for the sake of consistency throughout the book. The reader must allow me to proceed without constant recourse to experimental data since verification of psycho-analytic theory is not the subject of this effort; however, recalling the data of common observation will make these concepts seem no more than common sense.

The child is born with certain predispositions, strengths, and weaknesses. Some are bound to be large or small, bright or stupid, attractive or ugly, black or white no matter what life experiences they meet. The direct genetic transmission of such potentials is not always clear so we may lump together these relatively fixed limits for future development as consti-tutional. Such minimum and maximum limits for future psychological functioning are not nearly so clear so we tend to consider the major influences to be environmental or experiential. Perhaps we have gone a bit too far in such dichotomizing. It seems likely that the relative amount of stimulation to learn through award for achievement may play a much larger role in eventual intelligence. Nutrition effects size. Attractiveness may be enhanced by cleanliness, facial expression of emotions, style of dress, and the expecta-tion of being attractive.

In psychological development we may have gone even further in our attempt to separate mind and body. Our pres-ent attitudes reflect a belief that enough effort will make bad people good. Slum clearance, job rehabilitation, and increased education will remove the ugly sores in our midst and produce a society of well-adjusted and contented people. This is shown even more dramatically in our current debate on world peace and reduction in world tensions. If we could raise standards of living, be reasonable to our fellow nations and destroy our aggressive weapons we could live in harmony. War is unwanted and a mistake that could be avoided.

Perhaps the older belief, basic in Jewish and traditional Christian teachings, that man is born in sin and must be saved to live in peace is nearer to the real nature of man. Let us look at the newborn and see.

What we observe is a bundle of activity and energy. The child is born with this energy; he doesn't learn it. We note it is cyclic. The child becomes increasingly restless, thrusts about aimlessly, begins to whimper, then scream till the breast or bottle is available. As the baby hungrily gums and sucks the nipple, we observe a gradual cessation of activity. The pupils become smaller, finally pinpoint in size, and sleep ensues. This experience is repeated several times daily. We may say the child is motivated to this activity by hunger alone (and dampness, cold, too-tight clothing, etc.) but we also notice the energy invested in being relieved of the desire to achieve satisfaction. In fact, we notice from the very beginning of life how some children are much more active or kinetic than others and realize that this could not have been taught by experience.

It seems, then, that man is born with a basic drive or push that provides him with the necessary energy to stay alive and seek certain gratifications. Unfortunately, this drive or energy has been taken too literally in early psychoanalytic writings which imply a quantification of energy that could almost be expressed in ergs. Even though we cannot measure it, we can certainly see it and we will be concerned how this biological constitutional element is modified by human experience. To complicate things even further, the term "instinct" has been used to refer to this drive to live. More properly instinct would refer to those inborn tendencies to behave not modified appreciably by learning that we see in lower animals. Since we are referring to behavior tendencies, we are not concerned here with such obvious needs as breathing. The drives in man are also inborn and biological. However, the drive is felt as a propellant to action with the goal of removing the need to act or experience the drive. How this is accomplished is something that changes with maturity and increases in complexity and subtlety. The screech and random limb flailing of the newborn halted by the breast in mouth hardly seems related to that satisfied and contented feeling the adult has after he has accomplished something of value; yet it is.

In the beginning, the child demonstrates a mass reaction demanding relief. As the cramping abdominal sensation continues, the child increases his energetic activities. If allowed to continue longer, his actions become more frantic. Suppose we were to put such rage as now expressed in the body of an adult man. He could be a dangerous character indeed. While it is impossible to put ourselves into this situation, we have come to some conclusions retrospectively about the subjective world of the child at this point. At first he is all, omnipotent. He could be nothing but this since he has no comprehension of the world about him. He sleeps, feels increasing pressure to be gratified, gets restless, then signals for relief. Relief comes and he sleeps. Since he comprehends nothing but his own self and that but vaguely, he does not see the gratification coming from another. However, as he matures he repeats a peculiar experience many times: he wants, demands, then waits till he gratifies himself. Why does he delay? He notes the shadow that appears and ends the delay. Gradually, it dawns on him that there is something beyond himself. The "me" is those parts of the body, clothing and crib that are constant. The "not me" is those parts of the environment that disappear and reappear and do something to him. We also observe the constant finger play of infants. The fingers go into, onto and around all they can reach literally thousands of times. The infant gradually adds another piece of vital data: the one-touch world associated with those things not part of the self, i.e., "not me"; and the two-touch world that further defines "me." When one touches his own cheek he receives two tactile stimuli; when one touches his mother's cheek there is but one stimulus.

What we are observing is the first development of the sense of identity, or the ego. This experience is vital in helping us answer that most important of all questions: Who am I? Failure to answer this question has caused more human misery than any other combination of developmental errors. It is now believed that a basic unfolding of this sense of identity, or the ego, will occur whatever the psychological experiences; that is, there is a biological demand that this will happen. Nevertheless, left to biology alone the development may be hazy and lead to much later psychopathology.

During these early months of life, the child is aware increasingly of his separateness from the rest of the world and with this knowledge comes danger. No longer is the world limited to his own sensations, under his omnipotent and magical control. The sense of helplessness now develops when the wish for gratification is not instantly met. The longer the delay and the more frequent the experience of helplessness, the greater the panic and rage. Yet it is necessary for the infant to learn to face his separateness in the proper dose so he can develop the proper coping mechanisms. If not given enough chance to see himself as having an identity, the child attempts to prolong his phantasied omnipotence and is not prepared to move ahead towards maturity. If the sense of helplessness is forced onto the child beyond his tolerance, he feels overwhelmed, weak, and may even lose the hope of pleasure in closeness with others.

The sense of urgency, or the driving psychic energy, seems to be most gratified when sucking, being fed, made warm and sleepy. As the horizons enlarge, the child takes more notice of the parents. Their demands, punishments and love become known and the child responds to them. He moves more aggressively about his environment, seeking both to placate and be loved and to punish his parents for their demands or withheld affection. The child now becomes aware both of love and hate for the parents, i.e., he develops ambivalence. Bowel and bladder training become a convenient battleground. The feces may be presented to the mother as a prize gift for which she should be gratified and at other times is withheld from her when she is to be deprived and punished. The more relaxed the parents are about this issue, the less it becomes the focus for ambivalence. Unfortunately, many parents are still reacting to their own forgotten conflicts as children and make bowel training a big issue. They may insist the child perform when they demand it, forcing the child into excessive compliance or its opposite—excessive stubbornness and defiance. While the significance of bowel habits themselves should not be exaggerated, the character habits of over-compliance or stubbornness and parsimony may become dominant components of later interpersonal relationships.

During this phase of development, from about one to three years of age, the child is widening his scope of interest. He wanders about his yard, the house next door, and occasionally takes an expedition down the block. He learns the mother next door is to be trusted, dogs ears can be pulled, and that other children are fun to be with. Games are not well-defined and are limited by his lack of coordination, sense of time, acceptance of rules, and undeveloped feelings of cooperativeness. Mother remains his dearest object though father can be useful at times. Father is the person who runs big machines, not the person who feeds, bandages bruises, and tucks into bed.

From about three to six years of life a most important series of experiences develops. Nursery school and kindergarten bring many exciting and at times frightening experiences. The child is learning social rules, how to play cooperatively, how to share. He is also facing frightening experiences from within himself. We recall the infant is a bundle of violent energy, seeking expression and during childhood methods of living with this driving energy are being developed. At this age, the issue of being a boy or girl is now faced.

We will attempt to discuss this age without overdue emphasis on sexuality which has long repelled many skeptics and caused them to turn from all psychoanalytic formulations. Nevertheless, we must face our observations and we realize that the behavior of children at this age has definite linkage with later adult sexuality.

The little boy, like girls too, is most strongly related to his mother. His attraction to her now takes on a new aggressive characteristic. He moves toward her more assertively; he is her little man; he is proud of his power. There is also a biological shift of sensitivity and excitement to his genital organ so that his close contact with his mother results in something akin to the sexual urge we find in adulthood though the child has no conception of this adult sexual behavior. He also enjoys contact with father but this seems to be taking on a more competitive nature. He drives bigger cars than his father and has bigger guns. He shoots father dead when he comes home at the end of the day. As his competitiveness becomes more apparent, his phantasies of being more powerful become more transparent and his anxiety increases. The more aggressive he feels toward father the greater the threat of retaliation. We see here, then, a connection between the dangers of expression of the sexual and aggressive drives. The boy notes that his attraction for his mother places him more in the position of his father who also enjoys hugging and kissing mother and showing off his power before her.

This conflict between the desire to express his basic drives and the fear of the consequence gradually increases in intensity till the only solution open for a satisfactory resolution is renouncement of these drives. This is not an easy struggle to win and the result is often not too satisfactory. In fact, the basis for much of the neurotic disturbances and inhibited character formations that plagues adult life has its origins at this time.

To assist in this struggle the child develops a new agency of the mind, the superego or conscience. While some archaic development of this structure antedates the period under discussion, this time seems to be the crucial one. Originally the child was perplexed by "No!" and angry gestures or slaps. He gradually learned not to do certain things because he feared the pain of the slap or the disapproving face. However, he did not see the ethical issues involved. He feared doing "wrong" but didn't see it as wrong particularly if it pleased him to do it. In fact, he took the blows of the parent as acts of aggression and on occasion would hit back. If that was too dangerous he would hit his little sister or neighbor children or even his dog. He responded to prohibitions most effectively if the prohibitor was present.

Now, with the greater threat of the danger of his basic impulses, he needs a more efficient prohibition system. He is very attentive to the attitudes of his parents, both spoken and implied. If he can just know what his parents will allow, then he avoids the risk of making a serious mistake. Gradually he takes into himself the reproving glares, no's, and punishments and also the approving smiles and rewards. It is as if they now speak from within him and go with him wherever he goes—thus he is under the constant protection of his conscience against breaking taboos. We see, then, how the conscience aids the individual in controlling those impulses which would otherwise get him into serious risk. Unfortunately, some have too much or too little control.

A peculiar contradiction sometimes develops in this incorporation of parental values. Inevitably, to a greater or lesser degree, there is a lack of consistency between the stated moral position of the parent, his unstated but conscious attitudes, and lastly with his unconscious attitudes. The child assimilates some of each and also faces the differences of opinions between his mother and father, or between them and his friends' parents, school teachers, and even the community opinions. Parents may be more revealing to their children than they realize. A group of children are playing and one is a bully. The mother, knowing other mothers do not approve, tells her child to stop picking on the other children. However, a brief smile crosses her face first in appreciation of the masculine aggressivity shown by her "little man." Or, a father tells his boy to be assertive, not let himself be pushed around, but his son notices how passive his father is in the face of his mother's nagging.

We must not forget our little girls before we proceed. As was true of the boy, she is deeply involved with her mother. When there is the same biological increase in sensitivity of the genitals she gradually becomes aware of a sense of difference which is equated with inadequacy. This concept of "penis envy" has never been popular with feminists who violently deny any sense of inadequacy; in fact they mention all sorts of ways in which the woman is equal to or superior to the man. In a sense, this competitiveness is a confirmation. However, there may be some justification in suggesting its emphasis is a result of its observation by men. Others question how the little girl could be aware of such a difference. They are ignoring the obvious curiosity of children about their bodies and the bodies of siblings, parents, and other children.

The little girl's reaction is a mixture of disappointment in her mother and anger at her for her deprivation. After all, everything important comes from mother so why not this too. Sometimes the direct expression of genital deprivation is rather obvious. She may say she does have a penis or she may be jealous that her brother does things she can't, or even wonder why he can urinate standing up. She then makes a shift of attention to her father as the possessor of power who can make up her loss. There develops a rather obvious seduction of the father—long loving glances, climbing on his lap, wanting to be his best little girl. Obviously she is getting into a dangerous situation. She dare not become too apparent a competitor of her mother because mother remains a vitally needed person. Thus, like her brother, she needs all the controls over her impulsive nature she can find. To assist in this control she, too, develops her conscience to keep her from danger of too much expression.

Up to this point, childhood has been a time of much inner conflict and turmoil. The child is caught between wanting to explode with this true nature and the danger this would cause. These are years of frustration, rage, fear — night terrors, crying spells, violent behavior alternating with compliance and passivity. Hardly the wonderful years of childhood we look back towards with nostalgia.

From about six or seven to puberty, the child enters a new stage which is relatively more tranquil, at least from the intrapsychic viewpoint. The struggle to maintain control of impulses has been won and the child can turn his energies to the world around him. The little boy has decided the safest course is to placate father by mimicing him. He is interested in boys, men, sports, war and activity. He is not very interested in girls except to pester. The little girl has returned her attention to mother and plays house with dolls, wants to learn to cook and sew, and has no use for boys except to get them to pester her. This is the age when each sex learns what it means to be male or female.

As the child is now turned to a much wider experience than just the family, he learns what the societal demands are for general behavior, morality, and sexual identity. Of course, a major element in this is the transmission of cultural values from the parents to the superego of the child so that he comes to believe in those values as his own.

Perhaps his or her greatest task is to learn sexual identity which includes both intrapsychic and cultural elements. Some observers believe this task has become more complicated in recent generations, though proof for this is rather meager. Perhaps the role of father and man versus mother and woman was once more clear. Father tended the crops or went to the office or factory; mother had babies, cooked and cared for the children. Men were assertive, aggressive, matter-of-fact; women were sensitive, emotional, passive. Thus, the child had a clear picture of the role to be copied. Nowadays, women seem to be moving into male roles, demanding more rights, refusing to be so dominated. Men are a bit more feminine—they help in child-rearing, wash dishes, let their wives push them around a bit. As a result, problems in sexual identity may be on the increase. Many boys who know they are expected to be aggressive are not able to be so and little girls are taught they shouldn't be satisfied with being a homemaker but should have a career so they can "express" themselves.

As this period unfolds the child is gaining much in new social skills. Group loyalties develop, close friendships with neighbors, gangs and teams are formed, and heroes picked from the entertainment and sports world. The result is a lessening of the significance of the home and an increase in outside institutions like school, church, Boy and Girl Scouts, neighborhood centers, gangs, etc. The groups provide new outlets for aggressive and sexual strivings but under careful control. One sticks to the rules of the game and tries to be like everyone else. The fad phenomenon associated with the teens is beginning to develop. This is also a period of curiosity about the world, people, things that work, and animals.

These are truly the "happy days of childhood" as the child experiences real joy in learning new skills and facts, how to belong with his peers, how to be a man or woman in miniature. It is also a time when unfortunate influences in the social setting can begin to warp the child whose early years were not too secure. Up till this age the family was all-important and it didn't matter too much whether that family was rich or poor, black or white. Now the implications of social differences, prejudice, and poverty have their effect. This is also a time when malformation in the earlier years causes such fear of advancement into maturity that the child stays chained to intrapsychic conflict and cannot move out into the world.

Puberty ushers in that most painful of ages—adolescence. Adolescence becomes better understood when we realize the conflicts that were put aside from the age of five or six are reawakened now. The great upsurge in biological sexual drive forces the child to re-experience the attractions and fears he felt then. For the youngster who found a safe and nonpathological solution then, this phase is not too difficult. For the child who could not face the earlier time without massive denial of danger and of the urges creating the danger, this is a very stressful age.

What we are seeing in adolescence is something of the basic biological drives, i.e., man's essential nature—and the attempts at defense against these drives. As an adult, a balance will be achieved and adolescence is the time of experimentation to find this balance. At no other time in life is one so able to achieve such transcendental loyalties to a cause or friend, for a few moments at least, and soon after display such fickleness. A particular music style, such as Elvis Presley or the Beatles, becomes a more important target for loyalty than the Grand Old Flag or one's religion. But it lasts but a minute and a new star is born.

The basic drives burst forth suddenly and shock the adult whose short memory is a result of self-protective repression. Masturbation, homosexual experimentation, gang fights, promiscuity, and car theft are reflections of the animal inside and we are surprised this could have been just a child so recently. The defenses may quickly gain ascendancy and are shown by esthetic and philosophic preoccupation, pursuit of scientific knowledge, hyper-religiosity, and espousal of causes such as civil rights and pacificism. In most young people we see an alternation, some times so quick as to be unbelievable. In others whose early experiences gave them less strength for mature defense one or the other picture may predominate with little of the opposite side apparent. We then have the child who shows the impulses without adequate control and is delinquent or the child who shows only defense and is rigidly constricted and hides all creative potentials.

Gradually, adulthood is reached. We might define adulthood as that time when an adaptive balance is reached between impulse and defense. Unfortunately, by such a definition many people never make the grade. The failure to reach such an adaptive balance is the essence of immaturity. Having reached such a balance but then regressing to maladaptive techniques of defense is labeled mental illness. Such a view of immaturity and mental illness is very useful in explaining the diversity of human behavior we all see around us. We will review briefly some of the more common forms of maladaptation.

By immaturity we mean the individual has established a rigid manner of behavior where either the impulse is undercontrolled or over-controlled. The hyper-aggressive and antisocial person would be the example of undercontrol as would the sexually promiscuous or constantly self-gratifying. Some people show their over-control by excessive passivity, constriction of creativity, severe inhibition, and obsessive rumination. Sometimes deviations of sexual impulse, such as homosexuality and exhibitionism, are attempts to deny the dangers of adult normal sexuality.

Others show the strain of trying to maintain defensive controls which they feel are too weak over impulses they fear are too powerful. They suffer from neurotic anxiety which is simply a feeling of impending disequilibrium between impulse and control. This anxiety may be defended against by over-use of drugs or alcohol or by the development of symptoms such as phobias which are an attempt to localize the anxiety to specific situations that can be avoided.

For some, the capacity for defense is so overwhelmed they withdraw from any situation that would be provocative and substitute a phantasy world that seems safer and more gratifying. Others say the danger is not within themselves but in the world around them which then appears like a volcano about to erupt and peopled by dangerous and wicked individuals.

We must always keep in mind the quantitative differences between the mature adult and the immature or mentally sick. Sometimes this recognition is obscured by well-meaning propaganda efforts to make mental illness "just like any other medical illness." It really has little resemblance to the more standard physical diseases. Mental illness resembles disorders of chemistry and molecular structure much less than disorders of social structure and morality.

No matter how mature the person, this maturity merely reflects the stable equilibrium between basic biological drives and the learned defenses against these drives. Anyone can be stressed to the point he regresses to less mature and more desperate defenses and even to a breakdown of defense and emergence of the drives (or to withdrawal as a last ditch defense).

In our later chapters we will consider how sports and play can aid us in keeping a healthy balance between drive and defense. In this way sports becomes an agency encouraging maturity and helping in the maintenance of mental equilibrium.

In summary, we have traced the vicissitudes of the biological drives through the various stages of development and the formation of the ego protective mechanisms that help us maintain equilibrium. We have mentioned, only briefly, the maladaptive attempts to maintain equilibrium that we refer to commonly as immaturity or mental illness. Lastly we have hinted at the content of the chapters to come as they explain the value of play and sports in healthy adaptation.

REFERENCES

1. Arlow, Jacob A., and Brenner, Charles: *Psychoanalytic Concepts and the Structural Theory.* New York, International Universities Press, Inc., 1964.
2. Brenner, Charles: *An Elementary Textbook of Psychoanalysis.* New York, International Universities Press, Inc., 1955.
3. English, O. Spurgeon, and Finch, Stuart M.: *Introduction to Psychiatry,* Second Edition. New York, W. W. Norton and Company, 1957.
4. Noyes, Arthur P., and Kolb, Lawrence C.: *Modern Clinical Psychiatry,* Sixth Edition. Philadelphia, W. B. Saunders Company, 1963.
5. Waelder, Robert: *Basic Theory of Psychoanalysis.* New York, International Universities Press, Inc., 1960.
6. Wepman, Joseph M., and Heine, Ralph W.: *Concepts of Personality.* Chicago, Aldine Publishing Company, 1963.

Chapter IV

THE EVOLUTION OF PLAY AND SPORTS

IN CHAPTER III, we have reviewed the development of the personality from the psychoanalytic point of view. We have attempted to understand how the basic biological drives are forced into a compromise of expression by the demands of the reality of group living. Further, we have seen how failure to achieve a healthy compromise between the wish to express these drives and the demands of life may result in the development of pathological adaptive systems which we have referred to as immaturity or mental illness. In this chapter, we will discuss the use of play and sports as a means of both satisfaction of these drives as well as defense against them. We realize that the play activities of the infant are a far cry from the sports interest of the adult and we will view the evolution of play and sports from one end of life to the other.

While no two individuals play exactly the same, we sense that there is some consistency in play forms among individuals of a similar age. It is not surprising to us that there is much greater similarity in the play activity of the very young when we contrast it with the major differences of what is playful in the behavior of adults from one social structure to another. Obviously, as the influence of cultural mores becomes more manifest, the more basic and universal types of play are obscured by what is considered "fun" locally. Since there is so much similarity in the play activities of the young from highly variable cultural backgrounds, we suspect there is a basic significance of play activities which is more biologically determined than socially determined. Thus, as the cultural

[46]

limitations of what is play become more manifest, the basic biological components become more obscure.

As we recall, the first few months of life are spent in the gradual separation of the "me" world from the "not-me" world. This is the most significant step in social development that we ever face and, unfortunately, the one which is often faced unsatisfactorily. While one might not consider the apparently random activity of the infant as "play," it seems to be the precursor of all the play activity we will observe developing in later life. We remember that play is not frivolity but is very serious business. At this point we cannot really call it "play" in the most limited sense since play includes the realistic appreciation that this behavior is not reality. Such is not possible for the newborn infant nor the infant of a few months of age. Nevertheless, this serious exploratory behavior of the infant is gratifying to certain basic urges and comprises much of the waking time of the child.

Gradually this random activity takes on certain goal directed aspects. In the second half of the first year, the child becomes aware that those around him are not part of himself and he learns to perform certain actions which bring pleasurable responses from others adding to his own gratification. We note the hilarious reaction of the infant as he gurgles and smiles to achieve a loving response.

During the second year, the horizons of the child are much expanded as first he crawls and then toddles about expanding his environment. He is learning to manipulate, throw, knock down, pull down, and in various ways move those objects about himself at his will. He is very much aware of the people about him and runs or waddles towards them in pleasant expectation and then runs and hides from them in mock terror. We can see the play element since he is playing the game with those about him even though he knows there is not the danger he pretends. In fact, his play of running from the ferocious parent may be seen as his attempt to act out his real fears. By "pretending" that he is in danger and by learning to avoid this pretended danger, the child is developing the techniques of mastery over the real dangers he faces from the huge adult world. In a sense, this is like a counter-phobia which is an attempt to play out a dangerous role as proof that the real danger cannot overcome him.

One of the more interesting play forms we see in the second year of life is the game of "peekaboo." This seems to be a game that is played by children of all backgrounds — almost a universal play form. The child is playing out the game that people can be made to disappear and return at his own demand. We can speculate that the motivation to this is the attempt to master the anxiety that those people most vital to him, in this case his mother, will not leave him. What he is saying in the playing of this game is that he, rather than the mother, has control over her appearance and disappearance; thus, he does not run the risk of losing her. Since this is an anxiety which has its greatest intensity in the first two years, it is not surprising that the game of peekaboo ceases to be needed after the age of two.

We then enter a phase, a pre-Oedipal phase, where the child is much more involved with people about him and is rapidly expanding his horizons. He has not yet learned to be a cooperative social beast but sees himself as the center of the universe still and believes that anything worth having should be his own. Children at this age are grasping and grabbing and do not understand sharing yet. It is also an age when curiosity grows rapidly and the child moves out into his "community" seeking companionship with children. Up to this age, the child has preferred to be near parents and parent-like figures. Sometimes the child who does not have companions about him will manufacture fantasy companions or great interest is expressed in animals to take place of child companions. Now is the time when the child is beginning to play roles of power and we notice the child playing with toys which provide a fantasy gratification of great power. The little boy plays with trucks, fire engines, earth movers, and other instruments of powerful connotation. Sometimes play can be rather destructive. A seeming paradox is observed in nursery groups: the aggression of the children seems less controlled in the presence of adults. This is the age where the early vestiges of the conscience are forming. It appears the child gives back responsibility for impulse control to the adult who is present since he has not yet really made it his own control. When the adult is not there to assume such responsibility the child is forced to exercise it himself.

Gradually, the child moves into the age range where the Oedipal problems become more dominant. The result is an attempt to play certain adult roles and the wish to be powerful is more manifest. Playing with guns and shooting playmates and parents indiscriminately is great fun. The child is playing adult roles and trying to be like big people since he is very curious about what big people do. The child is becoming much more able to play cooperatively with others and with other children begins to choose up sides, chooses alternate roles of being the aggressor and the victim, and is very much turned to the world of play and fantasy. Nevertheless, we are now aware that the child can readily determine between the reality about him and the games of play in which he engages. We can say that this is truly "play." Since this is a time of such great internal stress, the child is more turned to internal fantasy and personal preoccupations than will be seen in the next few years which are much more social-oriented years.

The post-Oedipal years, say from six to twelve or thirteen, are turned increasingly to the outside world and those who people it. We see the receding significance of the family during these years with children now much more important

in the eyes of the individual. Now the child is becoming
interested in team games or games of cooperation. "Cops
and robbers," "hide and seek," and "cowboys and Indians"
are played for hours at a time. It is very important that the
child play the game according to the rules and violent argu-
ments ensue constantly during the course of play in an attempt
to chastise that one individual who does not play according
to the rules. Not to play according to the rules ruins the
game for everyone. If someone is shot and does not fall down,
what is the fun in shooting someone? We also note how the
child may play different roles in the games, being the cowboy
one time and the Indian another or the cop on one occasion
and then again the robber. It is quite obvious that the child
is acting out the roles of being the attacker and the victim so
that he can learn for himself that he is safe. He is safe
from losing control of his wish to attack and he is also
safe from the danger of being attacked since in his fantasy
world he has control over both roles. We can see how
important it is that the rules be obeyed so that this game
of repetitive mastery can have its counterphobic value. In
fact, there doesn't seem to be any particular point in winning
these kinds of games but rather that the game be played
out strictly to the rules. About the time that one group
seems to be conquering the other the children change around
their positions and go off again in entirely opposite role. We
also note how conventional these games are since the internal
need to solve the problems of aggression and victimization
run so powerfully through the psychology of all youngsters
at this age.

We still see elements of the fears of being abandoned and
lost in some games. Perhaps such games as "hide and seek"
or "kick the can" play out this fear. In these games we see
a division into those who are lost and those who do the
seeking. Perhaps this is a playing out of the theme that a
child is lost and is sought by the parent. Also central to these

games is getting "home free," that is, without punishment. The child runs away and is sought by his anxious parent but then returns home and is free of punishment. If he is caught, his punishment is to take the role of the anxious parent who must seek the lost child. Since the child must play both sides of the game, he learns both how it feels to be lost as well as the limits of how angry the parents can get when the child disappears.

Games which have a general title of "I spy" are common during this time. Here, some object is hidden in open view and the player of the game attempts to find it while those who are in on the secret may say such things as "hot" or "cold" as a person comes closer or goes further from it. Great honor comes from finding and chagrin comes from not finding. This reflects some of the powerful superego elements at this age that the child is attempting to master. Something of great importance has been lost or mislaid and it's the fault of the child that it is lost. Thus, he wishes to placate the anger of the parent by finding it in this game.

We might speculate about such innocent games as "drop the handkerchief" where the children gather in a circle and someone runs around behind and drops a handkerchief at the rear of one child. It is interesting that this is dropped behind the child and it has been suggested that this is related to continued attempts to master anxiety over bowel functions since the victimized child is shamed and also the wish to be rid of certain undesirable elements within the unconscious related to infantile urges. It may be the games of tag or "It" have some similarity here where the person who is "It" has something which is bad as if it is a disease or bad luck or impregnation which must be passed on to some less fortunate person. The child who is tagged acts as if he has been contaminated and all the other children run screaming from him recognizing this contamination.

At the same time that we are trying to find obscure symbolic meanings to the play of this age, we also recognize the sheer joy in the big muscle activity in which the child engages. The play of this time is running and jumping and rolling and falling without very much attempt at fine co-ordination. We have noted before that it has been postulated that this is one of the motivations to play activity—that is the sheer enjoyment of releasing energy through such gamboling activities. It is quite obvious that the excited, and sometimes hard to control, activities of the child of this age has certain similarities to the sexual excitement seen in adults.

Team games begin to come on the scene in the period from nine or ten to puberty. This is especially true in boys but also true to a degree with girls. There seems to be a gradual shift in girls towards the play styles traditionally associated with boys. The type of team game that is played will vary, of course, with what is the sociably accepted type of team game in that area. It certainly cannot be seen as biologically defined that boys of ten or eleven like to play baseball since boys in other parts of the world much prefer to play soccer or some other sport. Nevertheless, the common elements are getting together in a group, submergence of individual performance for the sake of the group, playing under strict rules, the sheer joy of activity and excitement of the game, and now a new element—that is, the wish to win. Up until this age, competition to win has not seemed too obvious. It's true that throughout the years after the earliest period of childhood that wrestling and tussling has behind it an effort to establish a pecking order among the children. Nevertheless a developed sense of competition does not seem to come into the open until this age. We suspect that the years of three or four to seven or eight were not years of comfort in further competitive activity when one considers how competitive a life it is intrapsychically for the child during the Oedipal time. It is only now when some resolution has been accomplished of the Oedipal problems that the child can turn his wish for competition into the world about him. The very fact that boys seem to be much more inclined to competitive activities now may be related to the observation that the sense of competition during the Oedipal years for girls is much less and her ties to her parents less constricted by taboo.

The team sports that children engage in during these years are not equated with the team games of the older youngster. This is a point that has been lost in many developments of organized sports for youngsters. There are still remnants of earlier ages such as in the games of cops and robbers. It remains that winning the game does not have the significance that it has to the adolescent. More important is playing the game according to the rules, having the chance for exuberant expression of aggression and social exchange with others, and the chance to play the role of aggressor and victim alternately. It is quite obvious when a group of boys gets together for a game of baseball or touch football on a corner lot that no one pays very much attention to the final score but is much more interested in running up and down the field.

We do see the development of some competitive games during this age where winning is the goal. Interestingly, these are not so much games involving teams but individual performances. Such games as marbles, archery, throwing contests, and the like do have as their goal besting one's peers. In contrast to group games, the social interaction here is diminished and the attempt to win much increased. Wrestling and general tussling now takes on a more real element as the children decide who are the tougher ones in the neighborhood. This is also an age where all varieties of fads are prominent which can be made competitive. Those of a few years of maturity can well recall the late thirties when thousands of children would line up in their various neighborhood centers or in front of theaters to see who could bounce a ball on the end of a rubber band off a paddle the most times without missing. Later on and more recently such contests as hula hoops and performances on skateboards have taken the prominent position in individual competition. There is no end to the forms that these various contests can take and fortunate is the manufacturer of some play item who catches the fad at its peak. Another interesting form of competition at this time is that of collection. Most any item can be the object including marbles, bottle caps, baseball cards, stamps, and so forth. Girls particularly enjoy collecting various kinds of dolls, doll accessories, and all the fancy paraphernalia that go with them. It is also intriguing to note the interest in the collection of autographs during this age. It is as if the person who gets the signature on a piece of paper has also captured some of the power or glamour of the athletic or entertainment hero.

With the coming of adolescence, we see competition for the sake of winning becoming a much more prominent component in games. While the necessity of following the rules continues to be necessary, now the outcome of the game assumes greater importance. By necessity, this leads to much better organization of play so that now organized sports attract much greater interest. It is during these years when team games with organized competitive levels have their values. One of the errors in adult supervision has been to impose the rules of adolescent team play onto pre-adolescent children. During this age, we recall that the child is struggling between the desire to remain a child and the drive to become adult. Thus, we may see some regressive play activities occurring at this time but under careful control. It is too frightening to the adolescent child to regress out of control and so we see the regression taking its form in conventional play forms. We mentioned fads as a common phenomenon in pre-adolescent activities but this is even more true now among adolescents although at a somewhat higher level of sophistication. We see it represented in strange manners of attire, speech, and social performances as each adolescent must mimic those about him in this little game. This is a representation of the pre-Oedipal and noncompetitive aspects of development. At the same time, the adolescent is also striving towards adult behavior and this is acted out in the more traditional competitive sport forms. We are very much aware of the disdain that may be shown by those who are more in the traditional mold shown toward those who emphasize the regressive forms of adolescent fad behavior.

This is also an age when a rebirth of old Oedipal strivings of a competitive nature predominates in intrapsychic life. It was noted before that during the earlier years, say between three or four and six or seven that the child did not engage so much in competitive sports. At this age, however, the need is to be able to develop a healthy competitiveness and sports activity is certainly a healthy way to accomplish this. Being successful in sports activity becomes a manifestation of manliness in the boy beyond almost any other type of accomplishment.

What we have been saying here about competitive sports and adolescent age is not limited to boys. However, girls do not seem so driven in the direction of competitiveness and we can relate this to the difference in the Oedipal years in girls as we noticed earlier. Still, girls do compete with each other but in other areas such as music, scholarship, homemaking skills, and personal attractiveness. They also compete in organized sports, too. In fact, there is a growing tendency to encourage girls to participate in competitive sports through physical education classes, YWCA groups, and church sports groups to name a few.

We will not attempt any sophisticated analysis of the significance of various team games at this time. As noted before, the type of team game that is popular will vary from one part of the world to another. Nevertheless, we do note a great interest in a particular kind of game which has as its object to conquer a guarded territory held by the opposition. This theme seems to predominate through games that are popular all over the world and would include such sports as lacrosse, soccer, football, ice hockey, field hockey, basketball, and probably a number of other sports forms. One can't help but wonder at some universal psychological element that lends such an air of excitement to a game that has this simple purpose. We can rephrase these games in the following way: [One group, the defenders, possesses a highly valued object, the goal. Their determination is to prevent the aggressors from penetrating or defiling this wonderful object. The role of aggressor and defender is interchangeable and now the aggressor has as its object to penetrate and violate, to overcome the defenders of the opposite inviolate territory.] The resemblance to the Oedipal conflict of the five or six year old child which has now been reactivated during adolescence is inescapable. We will not jump to conclusions that this is the real nature of these almost universal play forms but it is interesting speculation. It must have something that attracts interest since international soccer contests may be played before well over a hundred thousand spectators who will scream in excitement through the entire contest, sometimes bursting into riots that have claimed many lives if the rules are not followed as the throng feels they should be followed or if the game does not go the way the local partisans wish it. It seems the more violent the attempts to penetrate and violate, the more desperate the struggle to defend the inviolate territory, the more popular the sport. The better the violators and defenders, the more we like it as contrast professional football with amateur football. These games which have common to them the attempt to violate a goal differ from such a popular pastime as baseball. Attempted psychoanalytic formulations as to the significance of baseball are a bit far out and will not be repeated at this point. However, one notes that the games with the object of violating a goal are much more universal in their popularity and have even gained ascendancy in this country. While baseball remains The National Pastime, the total number of spectators are much greater at basketball contests.

During adolescence we also note the development of interest in individual competition rather than just team competition. Golf, tennis, track and field, and swimming attract great interest though the interest here is more limited to the participants as these sports seem to provide much less vicarious pleasure for the observer. It seems easier to identify with a group effort to defend a goal line than in who will break a serve.

We now enter into the adult period of life and the varieties of sports and play appropriate to it. It is surprising that this period of life has been ignored for the most part in past considerations of the value of play. Many agree that play in children is of great value in learning the rudiments of adult living. However, few have considered the significance of play for the adult.

In a later chapter we will go into more detail about play and sports as one of the institutions of modern life that are significant in preserving our society. Before we think of these social issues, however, we might complete our picture by seeing how the continuation of the need to maintain equilibrium in the younger person is continued in the adult.

That adults play can hardly be questioned. As a matter of fact, the play of adults may take on many forms that have little to do with sports as we usually conceive of sports. As pointed out by Huizinga, our modern society has tended to make more play out of such things as business competition while reducing the play element in other forms of social interaction.

Perhaps one of the most common forms of play among adult men is the play at war. It seems hardly a generation escapes this opportunity. Despite the horror and suffering of war, we recall how Huizinga portrayed it as a play form. If anyone doubts the significance of this even today, have they listened to war veterans recite tales of those wondrous and exciting years? Many a man whose life otherwise would be a continuation of humdrum from birth to death has this one bright chapter to look back upon. Obviously, the tales of war become so exaggerated by the passage of years due to arteriosclerosis and fantasy that we can never be entirely sure of what really transpired. Yet, for many, this brief flash of excitement is the one time in their life when they sensed some gratification of internal drives and the need for the sense of potency. The very fact that phantasy can cover over so neatly their actual performance which may have been merely one routine assignment after another, does not dim the importance of this period in their lives. Our society seems to agree with this as the veteran is accorded certain distinctions and provided with securities as if no matter where his assignment and how noncombative his experience he still qualifies as a true man and war hero.

Sports itself must gradually change to new forms. It is not the usual man who can continue to race up and down a basketball court. Rather, his sports interests begin to turn in two directions. The one direction is into more genteel activities and the other is into vicarious experience. The more genteel activities of sportsmen consists of such things as hunting and fishing, golf, tennis (of the gentlemanly variety), and bowling. Mostly these are activities which do not place such demands on aging cardiovascular system and arthritic joints, perhaps with the significant exception of skiing which is a much more recent phenomenon. Nevertheless, all these activities have as their goal the maintenance of a sense of potency, allowing gentlemanly competition with peers and enough expectation of success to bring the participant back time after time despite repeated failure. No matter how passive the occupation, how sedentary the style of living, each man can be his own athlete by occasionally breaking 100 in golf or upping his score in bowling. Even these accomplishments, somewhat like wartime experience, can be exaggerated so that phantasy can help maintain esteem. Activities of this sort are very useful outlets for aggressions which do not find too many such controlled outlets in modern society. In fact, one can participate in many of these sport forms up until quite advanced age without serious impairment. It should be emphasized that it is not so much an issue here of exercise as it is an opportunity to be competitive and release aggressive impulses. One can hardly call bowling significant exercise nor is riding around a golf course in an electric golf cart very much exercise. The fresh air of the eighteen holes is hardly offset by the stale air of the nineteenth.

The other means of gratification comes through vicarious experience. This is something we will also talk more about in a later chapter. There is no doubt the vicarious experience of sports and play has become very much the style in recent years. Of course, this is not a new phenomenon as we think back to the audiences that participated in the earliest Olympiads as well as some of the Roman spectacles. Fans have gathered at amateur professional sports activities in this country as well as abroad for many generations. In recent years, with advances in communication, this has become even more of a significant way to spend one's time. In fact, television has tended to draw spectators away from actual game observation to observation in an easy chair. Coverage of sports activities has been the near death of professional boxing though shortly after World War II it had seemed like a godsend to this sport of somewhat varied reputation. Unfortunately, the overexposure of professional boxing on television ruined the sport by its extinguishment of the local boxing clubs from whence the boxers that were to reach the bigtime had to be developed.

We're seeing something of the same risk in football and baseball. Television exposure of the "Game of the Week" has not been much help to minor league baseball. Why should one watch Decatur in the Three-I League in an ill-lit and uncomfortable ball park when they can sit at home and watch the Yankees on television? It is not so clear what the effect of television exposure has been to amateur football. Nevertheless, there has been considerable control of telecasts of the big-league college football contests to allow the smaller colleges to maintain some sports viability. After all, amateur though it may be, college sports must have a box office to survive. However, the tremendous new popularity of professional football is making an increasing number of people less enthusiastic about paying five or six dollars to sit in the rain behind the goal line on a board to watch old Siwash in its amateur attempts to defeat Paducah U.

Another interesting phenomena of vicarious sports activity is the new popularity of professional golf via television. Big league golf matches are now carefully contrived to meet time schedules of the television networks, and even play-offs have to be scheduled for those holes on the course which can be reached by TV camera. What a thrill to watch Jack Nicklaus drive the ball 300 yards down the center of the fairway! One can almost feel his own wrists cracking into the ball at the point of impact and watch the soaring drive from their own efforts. This is felt just as satisfying by the man who never hit a ball over 150 yards in his life as by the man who can regularly hit the ball 250 yards into the rough.

In summary, we have reviewed the evolution of play and sports from earliest infancy through the stages of childhood and adolescence and into the declining years of adulthood. We emphasize again the major theme that play does not cease after one leaves childhood but is an essential element in the healthy living of all adults, too. We will wonder later if it isn't better to have our kicks in sports than by having our kicks in less controlled ways.

REFERENCES

1. Albino, Ronald C.: Defenses against aggression in the play of young children. *British Journal of Medical Psychology, 27*:61-71, 1954.
2. Blumenfeld, W. S., Franklin, R. D., Remmers, H. H.: Youth's attitudes toward sports, the Peace Corps, military service and course offerings. Purdue Opinion Panel Report, 21 (3, no. 66), 1962.
3. Cahn, Paulette: The role of play in the development of fraternal relationships of an older brother. *Sauvegarde, 4*:40-52, 1949.
4 Desmonde, H.: The bullfight as a religious ritual. *American Imago, 9*:173-195, 1952.
5. Frank, Lawrence K.: Play in personality development. *American Journal Orthopsychiatry, 25*:576-590, 1955.
6. Friedmann, Alice: Observations in a play group of young children. *Individual Psychology Bulletin, 9*:25-30, 1951.
7. Greenacre, Phyllis: Play in relation to creative imagination. *Psychoanalytic Studies of the Child, 14*:61-80, 1959.
8. Hunt, W.: On bullfighting. *American Imago, 12*:343-353, 1955.
9. Keri, Hedvig: Ancient games and popular games: psychological essay. *American Imago, 15*:41-89, 1958.
10. Klein, Melanie: Infant analysis. *International Journal of Psychoanalysis, 7*:31-63, 1926.
11. Lambert, Clara: Identification through play. *Childhood Education, 25*:402-405, 1949.
12. Layman, Emma McClay: *Mental Health through Physical Education and Recreation.* Minneapolis, Burgess Publishing Co., 1955.
13. Lewis, Eve: The function of group play during middle childhood in developing the ego complex. *British Journal of Medical Psychology, 27*:15-29, 1954.
14. Millichamp, Dorothy A.: Another look at play. *Bulletin of the Institute for Child Study, 15*:1-13, 1953.
15. Peller, Lilli E.: Models of children's play. *Mental Hygiene, 36*:66-83, 1952.
16. Peller, Lilli E.: Libidinal phases, ego development, and play. *Psychoanalytic Studies of the Child, 9*:178-198, 1954.

17. Peller, Lilli E.: Libidinal development as reflected in play. *Psychoanalysis, 3:*3-12, 1955.
18. Philips, Richard H.: The nature and function of children's formal games. *Psychoanalytic Quarterly, 29*:200-207, 1960.
19. Rosenberg, B. G., and Sutton-Smith, B.: A revived conception of masculine feminine differences in play activities. *Journal of Genetic Psychology, 96*:165-170, 1960.
20. Sapora, Allen V., and Mitchell, Elmer D.: *The Theory of Play and Recreation,* Third Edition. New York, Ronald Press, 1961.
21. Siegel, Alberta E., and Kohn, Lynette G.: Permissiveness, permission, and aggression: the effect of adult presence or absence on aggression in children's play. *Child Development, 30*:131-141, 1959.
22. Stokes, Adrian: Psycho-analytic reflections on the development of ball games, particularly cricket. *International Journal of Psychoanalysis, 37*:185-192, 1956.
23. Sutton-Smith, B., Rosenberg, B. G., and Morgan, E. F.: Development of sex differences in play choices during pre-adolescence. *Child Development, 34*:119-126, 1963.
24. Volberding, Eleanor: Out-of-school behavior of eleven-year-olds. *Elementary School Journal, 48*:432-441, 1948.
25. Waelder, Robert: The psychoanalytic theory of play. *Psychoanalytic Quarterly, 2*:208-224, 1933.

Chapter V

SPORTS AS A SOCIAL INSTITUTION OF CONTROL

Upon the fields of friendly strife
Are sown the seeds
That, upon other fields, on other days,
will bear the fruits of vistory.

DOUGLAS MACARTHUR

Up to this point, we have reviewed the development of the individual and the evolution of sports and recreation forms as they fit in with this development. In this chapter we will see how sports and recreation can play an important role in the progression of the individual's relationship to his society.

First, we will enlarge somewhat on our understanding of impulse control. We recall that the development of maturity may be viewed as the development of creative ways to control basic impulses with which we are born. These impulses are essential to the vitality of a person since without them the drive or spirit of living would be lacking as well as the methods of survival and procreation. These impulses, however, if allowed full expression in their infantile form would make both individual and social group living untenable. Sometimes we are led to excuse this behavior on the basis that it is "childish." However, someone with an adult body who behaved endlessly in such a childish way would be considered a serious menace to society. It is fortunate that the person who has a right to be "childish," that is, the small child, has his energies packed in such a small package for everyone's safety.

The control of these infantile drives for aggression and

[63]

sexual gratification is the major responsibility of the *ego*. Since this term has been so loosely used, we will make clear at this point to what we are referring. The ego is not something in actuality nor something that can be found in a particular part of the brain. It is simply a group of functions of the mind that we find cumbersome to keep repeating and so lump them under one term. Among these functions is that of control of basic impulses and it is in this sense that we say that the ego has the major responsibility of maintaining such control. Other major functions of the ego include relating the person to outside reality, control of movements or motility, development of logical thought, and the expression of feelings of love and affection towards others.

Any threat of basic drives to emerge abruptly into action or even into the individual's awareness is seen as a threat to equilibrium. This threat is experienced as an anxious feeling which is unpleasant and motivates the person to increase his efforts at maintaining control or repression over these impulses. If this imbalance becomes too severe or prolonged, the person develops such severe anxiety that disability may occur.

To assist the ego in maintaining this control, the super-ego may act as an ally. We recall in an earlier chapter the discussion of the development of the sense of conscience as a taking within the self the prohibitions of the parents and to a lesser degree the social order. Thus, any impulse which we see as bad in the sense it would not be approved by our parents is fought off as strongly as possible. The ego left to itself might not see this impulse as dangerous or leading to disequilibrium. In the usual situation, the sense of disequilibrium and external danger that open impulse gratification would cause is paralleled by the feeling of badness so that the ego and super-ego are working hand in hand. Unfortunately, there are also occasions where this is not so and the super-ego is too prohibitive and strict leading to a constant sense of guiltness which is not in keeping with reality. When this occurs, the super-ego and ego are then in opposition.

The major protection of the ego is to keep the impulse out of consciousness, that is, repressed. This is hard work and requires great effort. Forgetting when it is a result of repression is not a passive experience but requires active expenditure of "energy." Obviously, the greater the risk of impulse coming into expression the greater the amount of "energy" that must be expended by the ego in a self-protective effort. Since the ego has so many other functions and only a certain amount of "energy" to utilize, other and more creative forms of behavior do not receive their necessary attention. It must be emphasized at this point that there really is no such thing as this "energy," that is, nothing that can be actually measured but rather that this is a construct to explain what we observe in human behavior. No one really doubts but what there is a very powerful driving force within people vital to their functioning but it is something which defies measurement or full scientific description.

If a person is forced to move to excessive means of defense against emerging impulses, he may have to adopt a mechanism which is maladaptive. In this sense, psychoneurotic symptoms are a form of self-treatment in that they are the means by which this defense is maintained. For example, if massive repression is maintained over almost any impulse expression, the individual becomes constricted and drab and allows himself rather little internal pleasure. He is vulnerable to sudden breakdown of control as there is little reserve left for crisis since he is maintaining such massive efforts at control even in the face of minimal demand. Another example of maladaptive defense would be to say that these powerful internal and frightening impulses are not really inside at all but are outside or in the behavior of other people. Such an individual would be constantly fearful of attack or provocation from other individuals, suspicious of their motives, and would see the world as a very dangerous place in which to live. Rather naturally, such a person would be hypersensitive, suspicious, and would prefer a life of isolation away from dangerous people.

Another technique has been devised which often goes hand in hand with the one mentioned above. If we can think for a moment that the impulse to be guarded against has a certain force, let's say 100 units of force, then we would have to utilize at least an equal amount of force of repression to stay in equilibrium. The possibility would be to allow some of the impulse to come to gratification, say 25 units worth, then we would be faced with the defense against only 75 units. This would be economical for the psyche. In a sense, one might say that this is a type of self-bribery. I will let my unconscious have a certain amount of fun for the sake of more comfortably maintaining control over my unconscious. It is postulated that each attempt at adaptation has a component of both the type of control utilized plus the partial release of the impulse in such a manner that allows us to fool ourselves.

Since social groups are composed of individuals, it becomes apparent that the group has the same problem as any individual multiplied by the number of individuals. The result is the development of certain types of impulse control by the social group to help each individual maintain his equilibrium. We will review some of these types of control and think of them as being social institutions vital to the stable functioning of the society. We will consider the social institutions of control as falling under three categories: absolute prohibition, suggested prohibition, and partial expression.

The social agencies of absolute prohibition include our police and courts. Certain types of behavior have been deemed so destructive to the best interest of the group that we have passed laws forbidding them. For many people this is adequate in itself and acts as a suggested prohibition. Unfortunately, for a minority this much be an absolute prohibition, particularly for those individuals who have failed to take within themselves the concepts of right and wrong that the social group proclaims. For them, the prohibition and its enforcement must be dramatic, absolute, and quick.

This suggests a significant social issue of our times. Sometimes we are caught in conflict between the rights of the group and rights of the individual. Through most of the history of men, the rights of the group have far outweighed the rights of the individual. This has been necessary to maintain public order and defense of the home territory as well as assuring that each one will have the bare minimum of the necessities for survival. Now, in our age of affluence, there is a great increase in concern for the right of the person. With this has come a weakening of the right of the group. While this is believed to be for the general benefit of all, it has certain drawbacks. We are observing this issue in the present controversy over individual rights in the courtroom. Some critics feel that we are more interested in the rights of the offender than those of the victim.

Since laws, the police to enforce them, and the courts to pass sentence have been developed for the general good, it may be that any weakening of the absolute prohibition of the law is risky. Since these laws have been passed, not for individual good but for good of the group, it may be that the rights of the individual in court are not important. Some have likened the courtroom to the stage on which is enacted a moral drama. The moral is that wrongdoing will be punished, absolutely, and quickly. This enactment of the drama over and over acts to enforce compliance with the laws on the whole group. In a sense, the criminal within each of us identifies with the criminal under trial. This is not such an issue for those people who accept suggested prohibition through the development of a strong conscience. For those who are responsive to this type of control, the fear of quick and absolute punishment for the breaking of the law which is the story of the courtroom drama may be very important. It has been suggested that it really isn't important what happens to the person on the stage of the courtroom but rather that the terrible certainty of the actions of the court must be emphasized over and over. However, this is an issue of great complexity far beyond the intent of this book or the knowledge of the author.

Control by suggested prohibition is much more important to the social group. Recalling how this effects individuals, we realize we are talking about the super-ego or conscience. We learn from our parents who learn from their parents what is the proper way to live. We become uncomfortable when the introjected voice of the parent scolds us when we begin to stray from the straight and narrow. Since these ideas of right and wrong are passed from one generation to another from parent to child, this is the means by which mores of a social group carry through time. These teachings are emphasized by religions faith, by commonly accepted social taboo, by teachings in school, and by peer disapproval of any breaking of the rules. This is particularly noticed in the play of children who are very anxious that the rules of the game be followed. Very often, arguing over the rules requires much more energy than the game itself and the outcome of the game seems a much lesser importance. Children in their play are learning the right way to do things. In addition to the more formal moral code, suggested prohibitions also includes the understanding of the ways that "the right people" live and our attempts to emulate them. We might differentiate simply between absolute and suggested prohibitions by referring to the first as "cannot" prohibitions and the second as "should not" prohibitions.

Let us now turn to partial gratification as a form of social control. Obviously, certain elements of absolute prohibition

and suggested prohibition decide what types of partial gratification we can allow ourselves within a particular social
group. The gratification in a limited sense of basic impulses
of the aggressive and sexual drives is experienced as a pleasurable thing whereas it would be experienced as dangerous
if the full drive was allowed expression. Thus, we must look
to things which are entertaining to find these elements of
partial gratification.

In fact, the very pleasure we associate with entertainment
is a result of this small expression of unconscious desire
which results in partial discharge of the desire followed by
the state of relaxation of tension. Because the struggle over
control is so much more a problem for the young and immature ego, it is not surprising, then, that pleasurable activities
play so much more a part of the life of the child. Unfortunately, many adults have lost the capacity for experiencing
very much pleasure, particularly if they tend towards being
an obsessive or ruminative type of person. The result is that
since they allow themselves so little pleasure, they have that
much more need to maintain strict control of themselves.

Because these pleasurable activities strike at the deep
needs of all individuals, there are certain types of pleasure
which have almost universal appeal or at least appeal throughout an entire social group. This pleasure through partial
gratification can be achieved through actual participation or
through vicarious participation. In the child the former
predominates whereas the second does in the adult. The child
plays his games of war with great spirit and this is a more
civilized person because of it. I do not share entirely the
concern of many that the selling of war games and toys and
the showing of violent scenes in movies and on television is
bad for children. In fact, it may be a useful outlet for them
to be able to play at such expressions of aggression. If such
outlets were not provided, the actual aggression they experience within themselves would be far more violent than

anything that could be portrayed in the worst television
program. Children will play at games of destruction whether
they are given toys appropriate for it or not and this is simply
a recognition of what kind of people we really are.

Sexual play becomes manifest in association with aggressive
play as children tumble and tussle about in great excitement.
This gives them an initial opportunity to experiment with
strange and little understood feelings which later on will develop into recognizable adult sexual feelings.

Adults, too, play as we mentioned repeatedly earlier in
the book. It is good that they do so as it is valuable equally
to adult as it is to the child to have an opportunity for partial
gratification of these urges. It would be foolish to suggest
that we would have more wars if we did not have play forms.
Certainly, wars are much more complex social convulsions
than that. As a matter of fact, as suggested earlier, war
itself becomes a play form. It seems a bit peculiar to suggest
that in some ways the destructiveness of war is a natural outlet
for wishes of people which would have to find outlet in other
ways. Unfortunately, there are no facts to suggest that we
have more troubles when we don't have wars since we have
never had an ample opportunity to find out for any long
period of time. It is noted that suicide and homicide rates
tend to drop during wartime as the aggressive needs of people
are satisfied through either actual participation or vicarious
participation in the war. Rather, it might be more appropriate
to reflect on whether war is a necessary form of behavior for
people which will defy ultimately all attempts at rational
resolution of the reasons for war. Perhaps people will make
war and then find excuses for it later. We have discussed
earlier the great excitement in the lives of people who have
been in the military service during wartime and how this often
stands out as the most exciting time in their life, though more
so in retrospect.

Certainly sports acts as a major outlet for aggressions of

the social group. By following the rules, the aggression is
not dangerous and qualifies as a game. It is generally con-
ceded that a healthy adult, especially an adult man, will lead
a more complete and wholesome life if he has an opportunity
regularly for some type of sports activity in keeping with his
physical stamina and financial abilities. There is certainly
a movement today to encourage greater sports participation.
Of course, the major emphasis is on the physical aspects of
it through the invigorating experience of exercise. The psychological side is given much less emphasis because it is understood much less well and is not so obvious. In this sense,
it seems that more valuable play will be found in sports
forms where there is actual competition and aggressive expression against opponents rather than mere physical exercise in calisthenics. Calisthenics have never been popular in
the United States where games are much preferred by all.
Fortunately, there are games within reach of all but the very
most decrepit. As a matter of fact, a vicious game of bridge
may be psychologically as beneficial for those who would
rather lie down when they think of exercise.

Participation vicariously may be of considerable benefit
as a means of partial gratification, too. One would not
believe that this is quite as satisfactory as actual participation
but still fulfills a very useful need in our society. Particularly
with greater age, we step back into the world of the observers
through retaining certain competitor rights in more gentle
games. Since we no longer have to battle so constantly to
maintain our position in the pecking order, we cease to
struggle so hard but can gain substitute pleasure from our
low rank in vicariously joining with our athletic heroes. There
is a basic difference between the participation of the adult
and boy observer since the boy may often evolve the fantasy
that he is the hero himself whereas the adult male knows
better. Nevertheless, he feels a surge of animal delight as
he sits in his easy chair watching a professional football game.

He particularly delights in watching the defensive lineman "red dog" and smash the adversary quarterback to the turf. We see some of this same animal delight in a crowd watching a boxing match. The audience gets restless and begins to clap rhythmically during a match between two skilled defensive boxers because everyone is there to see the brutality. The audience may be a bit sheepish about it later and join in the public outcry against the brutality of boxing. For a moment, however, a great surge of delight has been experienced through the vicarious expression of inner aggressivity.

To repeat, the opportunity to express these impulses through some partial means of gratification diminishes the amount of effort we must expend at repression and other types of control which are depleting of psychic "energy" and leave us less able to handle crisis and creative activities.

Much of the emphasis here has been on the aggressive impulse. Certainly the sexual drive has an equal need for control and expression. We can see easily the place for a vicarious experience of sexual thrill through watching movies or reading love stories or even pornographic literature. There is also sexual pleasure experienced in certain types of play even in the adult though this is not so obvious as the aggressive pleasure.

Sports has been called a great teacher of young people so we shall reflect on this for a moment. After all, it is very important that we be taught the proper forms of behavior if we are to be useful adult citizens. The rules of conduct of how to be a man, how to win and lose, how aggressive it is safe to be, how to participate with others for the common good, and how to be gentle with the adversary who is defeated are all types of behavior most important for us to learn. Equally important is the self-esteem that is developed in a growing youngster through participation in athletics. For boys at least no other accomplishment bolsters self-esteem as effectively as gaining proficiency in some sports form. The primitive hunter and warrior is not far below the surface of civilization. Not so much the adultation of the crowd is important here as the feeling of self-pleasure that comes from learning to master a skill.

Perhaps this has been no better stated than by Douglas MacArthur:

"The opinions I expressed at West Point on the infinite value of athletic competition have but intensified with the passage of time. It is a vital character builder. It molds the youth of our country for their future roles as custodians of the republic.

It teaches them to be strong enough to know when they are weak and brave enough to face themselves when they are afraid. It teaches them to be proud and unbending in honest defeat but humble and gentle in victory.

It teaches them humility so that they may always remember the simplicity of true greatness, the open mind of true wisdom, the meekness of true strength.

It gives them a temper of the will, a quality of the imagination, a vigor of the emotions, a freshness of the deep springs of life. It gives them temperamental predominance of courage over timidity, of an appetite for an adventure over love with ease.

It creates in their hearts the love of wonder, the undaunted challenge of events, the unveiling hope of what next, and the job of the inspiration of life.

Fathers and mothers who would make their sons into men should have them play the game."

One can hardly improve on this. It is agreed that General MacArthur was preoccupied with making of soldiers but what he said would be true equally in the making of a good citizen.

In summary, in this chapter we have emphasized the value of sports and recreation as a means of social control of behavior. We have reviewed the nature of impulse control in the individual and seen how this extends to the control of group behavior. Basic psychological impulses can be handled by absolute prohibition, by suggested prohibition through the teaching of what is right and wrong, and to a degree by partial gratification of the impulse in a form which is socially acceptable. Sports and recreation are particularly valuable as a means of partial outlet of aggressive and sexual impulses whether we are participant or observer. Sports also acts as a means of teaching the proper behavior of the group since sports participation is a model of participation in life.

REFERENCES

1. Arlow, Jacob A.: The reaches of intrapsychic conflict. *American Journal of Psychiatry, 122*:425-431, 1965.
2. Freud, Sigmund. Civilization and its discontents, in *The Complete Psychological Works of Sigmund Freud,* Volume XXI, J. Strachey, editor. London, Hogarth Press, 1961.
3. Hartmann, Heinz: Comments on the psychoanalytic theory of the ego. *Psychoanalytic Studies of the Child, 5*:74-96, 1950.

Chapter VI

SPORTS AS A THERAPEUTIC TECHNIQUE

Recreational therapy may be defined as the medical employment of free play exercises, and activity to meet treatment aims.—JOHN EISELE DAVIS

Up to this point, our emphasis has been on the utilization of recreation and sports to maintain the emotional health of both the individual and society. In this chapter we will consider the use of sports and recreation as a therapeutic technique in the treatment of the person already ill.

It's important to recall our discussion in previous chapters, perhaps to the irritation of the reader. Nevertheless, the concept of psychic equilibrium between the basic impulses and the controlling forces of the mind is of essential importance to all our discussion.

We can consider mental illnesses as we did in an earlier chapter as disequilibrium. The milder type of mental disturbance, the psychoneurosis, is an uncomfortable state because of the imbalance between the impulsive life and the controlling mechanisms. In an attempt to maintain or establish new equilibrium, certain maladaptive techniques of repression and control of basic impulses are utilized which gives a psychoneurosis its particular picture. The so-called character or personality disorders are conditions in which a maladaptive way of life has been established and which is manifested in one life situation after another. An example is the utilization of a pattern of excessive control of impulse in a noncreative way such as by constant obsessive preoccupation that leaves the character rigid and unprepared for new stress. On the other hand, the character disorder may be

[75]

manifested by a lack of adequate defense with periodic out-
bursts of antisocial rage or sexual impulse.

The psychoses are evidence of chronic disequilibrium where
either the impulse may be more manifest as in a manic
psychosis or the defense exaggerated as is so often seen in
schizophrenic withdrawal. The essential difference between
the psychoses and the other conditions is the greater disre-
gard to external reality in the psychoses which gives them
their peculiar or "crazy" coloration when viewed by those of
us who still maintain adequate contact with demands of
reality.

Psychiatric treatment consists of many different techniques, some of which are new and unproven and others of
which have been in operation since the earliest Greek physicians. The concepts embodying vigorous play, healthful
rest, and nutrition are time honored as is the belief that
humane care and kindness are the most important medi-
cines for the emotionally ill. As medical science has pro-
gressed, more and more sophisticated types of chemical
medication have been developed which have as their goal
the quieting or tranquilization of the patient. Such a technique does not provide a more mature technique of living
but helps the patient maintain control over impulses too
powerful for him or the anxiety aroused by his serious state
of chronic disequilibrium. The psychological therapies have
come into prominence in recent times, primarily because of
the influence of Freudian psychoanalysis. However, these
more sophisticated psychological techniques are not so different from older concepts of humane care, kindness and
suggestion.

Psychoanalysis proper has as its goal the investigation of
the defensive methods of the mind with a shift towards more
creative defenses such as sublimation as the hoped for end
result. It should be emphasized that the goal of psychoanalytic treatment today is not the uncovering of old trau-

matic events as was true in the early history of psychoanalysis but the study of the defensive functions of the mind.

A word might be said about sublimation as a technique of self-protection. By sublimation we mean the control of basic impulses by allowing them into expression but diverted and altered in keeping with the demands of reality and the allowances of our conscience. Thus, the power of the impulses is utilized for successful and creative living. Economically, this is far superior to the techniques of repression where much of the "energy" of the mind is utilized in self-protection leaving one inhibited and constricted. The aggression of the surgeon, the voyeurism of the psychiatrist, and the smearing of the artist are useful to society.

Valuable as psychoanalytic treatment has shown itself, it is applicable to a very small portion of the people who are mentally ill. Partly this is because there is such a shortage of psychoanalytic practitioners that they can provide this type of care for a very small number. In addition, the problems that so many people suffer from would not be benefited by this type of treatment because of the demands for a basically healthy potential, the intellectual rigors it demands, the sacrifice in time and money, etc. People suffering from severe impulse control problems, from too rigid neurotic character defenses, or from psychotic withdrawal are not good candidates for such treatment.

As a result, the psychological treatments most widely used are referred to by a number of terms such as brief psychotherapy, supportive psychotherapy, psychoanalytically derived pyschotherapy, and a number of other similar terms. In fact, there is only a gradation from pastoral counselling, casework treatment by a social worker, to the nonpsychoanalytic psychotherapies, and finally to psychoanalysis itself as the most complex of such psychological treatment techniques. Because the brief psychotherapies are much less time-consuming, they are applicable much more widely. Also, they allow a greater range of activities on the part of the psychothera-pist and so can be used in those cases where the emotional state is too fragile to allow investigative work or where the individual is lacking in understanding, or acceptance, or in intellectual capacity to undergo formal psychoanalysis.

We will consider the formal use of recreation and sports as a therapeutic technique as it is applicable to the treat-ment of small children, adolescents, adult patients, and elderly people. Recreational therapy can be used for both patients requiring hospital care as well as for those treated in clinic facilities.

Play therapy with children has developed as a part of psychotherapy of children. Since small children may not be able to express conflicts in verbal terms or develop verbal insight, it has become very useful to encourage them to participate in certain games. The way in which a child plays with dolls may be of important diagnostic implica-tions. It also allows him a safe expression of impulses towards parent figures and siblings that would be impossible in real life. So traditional has this approach become that most any-one doing psychiatric treatment of children will have a playroom as a large part of the office facility.

The child is ordinarily given a wide variety of playthings such as dolls and dollhouse, crayons, blocks, cars, guns, etc. He is encouraged to do as he will with these things within reasonable social limits; meanwhile the psychotherapist is carefully observing and occasionally asking questions about the child's behavior. Some children will be very reluctant to engage in free play because of fear of the consequences but most will freely engage in play after they know the psychotherapist.

It is very enlightening to watch a child of three or four arrange the group of dolls in a dollhouse. Usually the dolls are provided in such a way that a child may choose stand-ins for usual family members. One can then see the arrangement and the prominence given dolls that represent the mother, father, brother, sister, and other important people. A child who could never say anything about hated sibling rival may treat the sibling doll very roughly or push it out of sight and pretend it does not exist. The child may then choose the doll to represent itself and put it in close proximity with the mother doll. Having the chance to act out these impulses is then followed by careful and friendly talk about the dolls and after a time this may shift to talk about the real people represented. Not only does the doll play give diagnostic impression but also acts to relieve considerable tension in the child. Sometimes drawing is a form of play most suitable for the child and all sorts of gruesome monsters may be the result. Some children are so constricted that they can barely make lines on the paper whereas others are so out of control that the picture is a smudge of wild colors without any outline to the drawn figure.

In older children, the play may be more active. This may be true particularly in residential treatment centers for children or in playground recreational facilities which are for emotionally disturbed children. The children from six or seven up to puberty will be encouraged to engage in group games with careful limit to the amount of competition for the more shy. Again, much is learned about the unconscious feelings of the child through observing his play and also much is gained in the way of tension release through participation. It is very important that there be a protective adult present to see that the play does not get out of hand. We recall that in smaller children the presence of an adult may actually result in more aggressive play but this is not so true in older children who feel relieved that someone is there to help them maintain law and order.

Neighborhood recreational centers have long been advocated as an important tool in working with disturbed juvenile patients. Some have gone so far to suggest that the reason we have juvenile delinquency is the lack of such healthy outlets for youthful spirits. This is obviously a gross over-simplification when one considers the complexity of human behavior and the multitudes of factors leading to its disturbance. In fact, in the wrong circumstances, the recreational center may serve as a collecting place for juvenile gangs and an area they consider their own territory to be protected against the ravages of outside gangs. Nevertheless, social workers, court workers, and child psychiatrists who work with juveniles feel that the opportunity for large motor activity for boys especially and girls, too, is a vital component to the program. It would be nearly impossible to maintain a group of young people in either a residential center or in a day center without an opportunity for much activity. Exuberance of the young is too great to be kept in the bounds of group therapy or in special education classrooms.

Of particular importance in working with the adolescent patient is the development of team sports. Youngsters before this age are less prepared for such activities but teen-agers may get considerable increase in self-esteem for belonging to a team. We will talk more in the next chapter about the problems and abuses in this area. It is quite important in using recreational therapy to emphasize the team participation for all rather than the need for victory at all costs. To avoid this problem, participation in individual sports is encouraged: swimming, tennis, ping pong, and other such activities.

Most of the recreational therapy utilized in the treatment of mentally ill adults takes place in hospital facilities. Particularly since World War II the presence of an active recreational therapy program is considered essential in any mental hospital. The Veterans' Administration has been the pioneer in such techniques but they have been readily adopted by most state hospitals and private psychiatric sanitaria.

More often than not the recreational therapy program is included under occupational therapy though with specialized recreational therapy personnel. In state and federal civil service, there are specific positions allotted for recreational therapists with varying requirements including a college degree, usually in physical education, for the directors.

Recreational therapy programs in mental hospitals have not always been organized with the proper goal in mind. Too often, the program is more one for the sake of diversion and filling time and utilizes volunteer help or untrained recreational therapists. The recreational therapy program should be developed with an understanding into the nature of mental disturbance and programmed in such a way as to fit in with the other therapeutic modalities. No one treatment technique in itself will be adequate to result in recovery whether it be drugs, psychotherapy, psychodrama, electric shock, occupational therapy, recreational therapy, or any other "therapy." Sometimes in the very large hospitals such as state hospitals, a lack of communication between various members of the staff results in pulling and tugging the patient in various directions in uncoordinated and often self-defeating way. This is being overcome to a degree by the recent trend to break down even the large state hospitals into small treatment units.

An essential part of the treatment group whether it be a small private facility or a treatment unit in a large state hospital is that there is a constant communication in cooperation between the staff members. This may be accomplished at a daily morning staff meeting where all members of the professional team are present, each with a responsibility to speak out about his observations of the patient, his recommendations for further care, and his criticism of the direction other parts of the treatment team seem to be pulling the patient. This is a particular problem if a large number of volunteer personnel are used since they are not

available for such staff meetings and do not have the professional background or feelings of competency to allow
them to participate. It is very important in administering
any group of volunteers in a recreational therapy program
to have good control over them and a well thought out
program of orientation and instruction. It is not enough
just to have a volunteer come in and take patients on a walk.

In the days of great enthusiasm over the new found technique of recreational therapy, there was a tendency to over-
emphasize some of the symbolic meaning of recreational
activities. This reached a point where a particular type of
play would be prescribed in keeping with the patient's unconscious needs as carefully as one would prescribe medica-
tions or make psychotherapeutic interpretations. The result
of this was to stultify recreational therapy to a degree since
every move of the staff and patients had to be carefully
scrutinized and wondered about. It also led to the use of
rather sterile and formalized prescriptions since it was impossible to really know for sure what would be best for the
patient and the prescribing psychiatrist felt obligated to
meet the style of the times. An example of his would be
the treatment of depressed patients. Since psychoanalytic
formulations lead one to the belief that depression is largely
a result of internalized and self-directed rage, it became necessary to force the depressed patient into aggressive out-
bursts. Further, because of self-hatred and self-punitive needs,
he was encouraged into degrading activities both for their
punitive value and also for their provocative value to force
him to get angry. Unfortunately, while internalized rage
may be a common factor in many depressed people, it did
not take into account the unfortunate fact that many depressed people are very shy, inhibited people with terribly
low self-esteem. The above formulated recreational program
would not prove very satisfactory for them.

It's now a more relaxed recreational program that we

prescribe for our patients. The emphasis is on the personal interaction between patients, and patients and staff, that can be encouraged by recreational program as well as the value of the play form itself. In addition, the learning of new skills in a person who felt he had no abilities whatsoever is a major step towards improving self-esteem. This has been a major value of occupational therapy where a person who sees himself as ugly and awkward is delighted to discover that he can make a reasonably good pair of leather mocassins, or weave a pretty rug, or even form and paint a very attractive ceramic vase.

Of course, some individualization must occur and this is the reason for the constant communication between staff members. Schizophrenic patients form the largest single group of patients in our mental institutions and require rather special handling. At the same time, no two schizophrenic patients are quite alike and even though one might formulate a program for schizophrenics there would still have to be consideration given to the particular patient and his relative state of withdrawal, suspiciousness, and break with reality. A very withdrawn, perhaps mute and posturing schizophrenic, is not the one to invite to join the ward softball team. However, he may begin to show some interest when partially submerged in a swimming pool. He may enjoy, or at least tolerate, having a ball thrown gently to him or take some pleasure hitting a celluloid golf ball. Of greatest importance is to investigate with him what he might like to do, not by asking him, but by directly offering him with encouragement some type of activity. The less regressed schizophrenic patient will enjoy games much more like a normal person and will be insulted if one offers him too primitive an activity which suggests to him how sick he really is. Nevertheless, because these people have retreated so violently from the competition of living, it is generally better to avoid competitive sports for them but rather encourage them to activities which give them large muscle exercise and a chance to develop some new self-esteem. Obviously, individual sports activities may be preferable for a person who is too withdrawn to join in with other people with very much enthusiasm. Sometimes calisthenics is a very good approach to this type of patient.

In one large mental hospital, on the staff of which I served, a very interesting program was developed utilizing senior physical education students from a nearby large state university. This was part of a credit course for them in which they were carefully supervised. Most of these students would become coaches and teachers of physical education and only a small portion of them would ever go into recreational therapy as a profession. Nevertheless, because of their enthusiasm in the engagement in physical activity, they were able to bring some inspiration to patients. The program consisted of their being assigned, singly, to a small group of five or six regressed schizophrenic patients, usually young men. These were patients who had had very little personal interest shown in them over the years and gradually had slipped into a torpid state of self-preoccupation. The program consisted of a gradually increasing program of calisthenics and then turned to shooting baskets in the hospital gymnasium. At no time was there any competition allowed beyond the competition that each patient would create for himself at the level he could accept with his fellow patients. While this did not result in any dramatic recoveries, it was a very useful program in bringing these patients back to some interest in dealing with their environment. Added to other therapeutic modalities, it was a step in the right direction.

The use of team sports in mental hospitals is open to some question by many observers. Too often, the person in charge of recreational therapy is so interested in competition and winning that he does not realize that this is not the goal of the recreational program. The result is to create a problem very similar to the one found in schools where the recreation becomes something for only the best performers. Obviously, it is the responsibility of the medical staff to see that the recreational therapy program is aimed towards recovery of patients rather than in developing a winning ward team and this is facilitated by the close communication recommended above.

For patients suffering from conditions where there is not the withdrawal of interest from the environment, a broader program can be utilized without as much concern that any harm will be done. Psychoneurotic patients and patients suffering from alcoholism and other forms of addiction will generally have recreational patterns very similar to the general population. The value to them of an active recreational program is similar to the value they have for any person. It has the additional advantage that life in a psychiatric facility can be tedious and energies are not given many opportunities for expression. As a result, a very active day in occupational and recreational therapy leads to a more comfortable patient group and probably to an earlier discharge. Many patients are rather surprised when they come to a psychiatric hospital since they anticipate coming for a rest. This has often been suggested to them by their family or their physician. One notes this most dramatically in a psychiatric unit in a general hospital where patients may be transferred from a general medical bed to the psychiatric unit and be told to get out of bed, get their clothes on, and play volleyball. It comes as rather a shock to them though obviously this would not be requested of them unless they were able to undergo such an experience.

While on the subject of the psychiatric units in general hospitals, it should be pointed out that they are now admitting more mentally ill people each year than all the federal and state psychiatric facilities combined. For the most, these are short admissions of relatively acute patients.

Since the units are generally small, twenty to forty beds, it is not possible except in the largest general hospitals to provide very advanced recreational opportunities. A swimming pool or a gymnasium is lacking unless it can be obtained by contract in a local school or YMCA. Quarters are generally cramped and it may require considerable ingenuity to develop any recreational program. Also, with such a small number of beds, it may not be feasible to have a full time recreational therapist and often the occupational therapist will double in this role with the help of the nursing staff. Nevertheless, much can be done by such simple activities as a brisk walk once or twice a day, calisthenics each morning, and such games that require relatively little space as ping pong and shuffleboard. To add a bit of zest, perhaps once a week the patients can go for a swim and have some gymnasium activities in a nearby facility.

Where team games are utilized, there is a certain limit to the type of games that will fit the patient group. Softball is naturally the preferred sport in the warm months but it has the disadvantage of a good deal of inactivity much of the time even for the active participant. On the other hand, basketball may be a bit too vigorous especially when it is hot. The result has been that volleyball has become a rather popular sport for recreational therapy. It requires less room than basketball and has the decided advantage of bringing all participants into active play. In addition, it does not require advanced athletic ability to play reasonably well. It has a slight hidden advantage, too, in that playing volleyball does not carry quite the same implications as playing the more popular and more highly valued team sports. One can be a poor volleyball player and not suffer too badly in his self-esteem but being a poor baseball or basketball player may carry a greater weight. One interesting thing is observed in utilizing a volleyball, particularly in a small enclosed space. One will note that certain types of patient may be reluctant to participate. This may be the paranoid and very anxious patients. Further questioning will reveal that these patients do not mind playing when they are in the back line but become very uneasy when they are in the middle or the front line. Since the paranoid patient is very fearful of being attacked, perhaps sexually, it is not too surprising that he prefers to be in the safe rear line where all of his possible attackers are in front of him. Unfortunately, the game requires moving from one line to another and this sometimes has to be modified where a large number of such patients are participating.

The older patient presents an especially important opportunity for recreational therapy. With the younger patient, we assume when he recovers that he will go back to an active life. Such is not true of the elderly patient and all too often his recovery means to go back to a dreadfully lonely and unrewarding existence. Because our code of behavior has developed in us the idea that to work is to be useful and valued and to play is to be frivolous, we have come to the conclusion we should stop playing when we leave childhood. As long as we can keep busy working during our mature years this may not present such a severe problem. However, in the retired person who can no longer work, he faces a very real problem of heavy time. It has been so long since he played that he may have lost the skill to play as well as the inclination.

As a result, a recreational program which takes into account the age and financial abilities of the patient is most important for the elderly patient. The goal is not only to lead to his recovery at the time of his illness but to teach him some games that he can play after he leaves the hospital. Such games as shuffleboard, darts, and horseshoes are good examples of the type of skills that can be taught. It is most important that these also be games that are within the financial and geographic possibilities for the patient. It would not be very healthful to encourage an old person on very limited income and without much transportation to play golf or even to enjoy bowling.

Because the older patient is often suffering from mild to severe brain damage with resultant poor memory and occasional disorientation, the skills taught should be repetitive and simple enough that it does not require any intricate rule comprehension. Obviously, it wouldn't be too useful to encourage this patient to take up chess if this is a game that he has not previously learned. Table games and card games are very fine for older people to learn. However, in talking about recreational activities we are emphasizing games which require some physical activity as the patient can tolerate since this tends to prolong the vitality of the patient. It is very surprising to some patients how much energy they have left. Many an old person has been first quite doubtful and then quite excited by making an attempt at playing some game where there is physical exertion.

To complete the value of this program for the elderly patient, they must be connected to some facility after they leave the hospital. They might not have the knowledge where to go to find the opportunity to play games or may be too shy to initiate this themselves. Most communities of any size now have Senior Citizen facilities where the emphasis is on active recreation with people of equal physical ability. Such facilities may include not only play activities but also sheltered work opportunities which are a wonderful means of increasing self-esteem in the person who feels his life has lost all its usefulness.

One point may be made though it probably is self-evident to most people. In playing games with emotionally ill people, whether children, mature adults, or the elderly, it is most important not to be condescending. Sometimes a well-intentioned but inexperienced recreational therapy staff member will feel that he is helping a shy and withdrawn person by not trying too hard to win, in fact letting the other person win. While I've expressed earlier grave doubts about the wisdom of engaging such a person in a competitive game, if such is to be the activity there must be no fraud since the patient will be very much more aware of this. Any "throwing of the game" will act as a further humilitation of the patient. I recall a somewhat exaggerated example of this. A young and very sincere and conscientious nurse was playing checkers with a withdrawn catatonic schizophrenic girl. The nurse noted that the patient would miss obvious opportunities to jump her checker and so she felt obliged to not take advantage of this and would pass up opportunities herself to jump the patient's checker. The patient was quite aware of what the nurse was doing since the nurse had erroneously assumed that the patient was too much out of contact to notice. The effect was to make the patient quite anxious since her failure to jump had not been through any lack of attention but through her fear of such an act of aggression. By the nurse trying to "be easy on her," the nurse was confirming to her how dangerous it is to be so aggressive. It would have been much more reassuring to the patient for the nurse to have gone ahead and jumped her checker and told her that it was all right for her, the patient, to do the same.

In summary, we have reviewed briefly various modalities of psychiatric care including recreational therapy. It has been emphasized how recreational therapy is an important part of the therapeutic arsenal but will be important only where it is correlated with the rest of the treatment program through close staff communication and cooperation. We have discussed some of the sports and recreational activities that are appropriate for youngsters, adolescents, mature adults, and the elderly.

REFERENCES

1. Anderson, Harold H.: Psychological aspects of geriatric recreation. *Geriatrics, 14*:742-747, 1959.

2. Cowell, Charles C.: Mental-hygiene functions and possibilities of play and physical education. *Elementary School Journal, 50*:196-203, 1949.

3. Davis, John Eisele: *Clinical Application of Recreational Therapy.* Springfield, Thomas, 1952.

4. Layman, Emma McCloy: *Mental Health Through Physical Education and Recreation.* Minneapolis, Burgess Publishing Co., 1955.

5. Maclean, Janet R.: Psychiatric aspects of leisure. *Journal Indiana Medical Association, 57*:896-903, 1964.

6. Martin, Alexander R.: Urgent need for a philosophy of leisure in an aging population. *Journal American Geriatrics Society, 10*:215-224, 1962.

7. Menninger, William C.: *Enjoying Leisure Time.* Chicago, Science Research Associates, 1950.

8. Morris, William E.: Recreation and mental health. *Mental Hygiene, 45*:360-366, 1961.

9. Olson, William E., and McCormack, John B.: Recreational counselling in the psychiatric service of a general hospital. *Journal of Nervous and Mental Diseases, 125*:237-239, 1957.

10. White, Paul D.: The advantages of physical fitness. *Illinois Medical Journal, 116*:185-187, 1959.

Chapter VII

MISUSE AND ABUSE OF SPORTS

We think we have reached a crossroad. We can continue our downward path for our young people by permitting some coaches and parents to glorify themselves with winning teams; with only the very best participating; with too few carrying the load; with too few developing their physical capabilities and with fewer or none developing fair play and good sportsmanship; or we can demand that ALL young children learn, practice, participate and have fun.—FROM THE ATHLETIC MEDICAL ADVISORY COMMITTEE OF THE ACADEMY OF MEDICINE OF CINCINNATI

THE ABOVE quotation from a group of physicians interested in the medical aspects of sports may seem a bit too critical. By now, it must be quite clear that the author is very much in favor of sports participation for the mental health benefits it brings. However, I suspect the same thing is true of this group of physicians and so we must wonder why their gloomy comments.

Anything which is good in moderation can be done to excess or in ways which are not healthful and this certainly applies to sports and recreation. Thus, in this chapter we will look at the other side of sports participation and concern themselves with some of the misuse and abuse of sports, most particularly as it affects our young.

It certainly is not a new observation since this has been stressed for a long time that overemphasis on varsity sports and winning can be carried to an unhealthy extreme. Many feel that this is true today in our schools. Is it possible that the glorification of the top athletes, the so-called star system, has been important in creating a spectatoritis among Americans interested in sports? Certainly in school the tendency

[91]

has been to emphasize the varsity. The student who is interested in sports but does not have too much ability, particularly if he attends a very large school, soon must face the fact of his failure when he cannot make the team. From then on, his tendency may be to watch from the stands since participation in intramural sports seems a pale substitute.

It has been said by a number of observers that Europeans are much more interested in general participation in sports and one might wonder if one factor is that there is much less emphasis in European schools on the star system. Rather, everyone is encouraged to participate without the sense of failure which comes from "not making the team."

On the other hand, there is a great increase in the emphasis on intramural sports and physical education in our schools today which seems to be a counter observation to the above. In colleges, for example, the income from the varsity football team may go a long way towards supporting much of the intramural sports program as well as other varsity sports. Probably when the young person is of high school age or above the situation does not loom as a serious one since whatever sports interests he has will find some expressions at this time. Rather, the problem may be a more severe one in the younger students, particularly the pre-pubertal students.

This is a point on which there is a great deal of controversy. A brief sampling of the expert opinion which speaks out against undue emphasis on competitive sports in pre-adolescent children would include the medical group in the paragraph at the head of this chapter, Doctor James E. Simmons of the University of Indiana, John Eisele Davis who is a national authority on physical therapy, the famous tennis teacher Jean Hoxie, the pediatrician Doctor J. L. Reichert, the policy statement by the Committee on School Health of the American Academy of Pediatrics, pediatrician Doctor Thomas E. Shaffer, pediatrician Doctor R. A. McGuigan, and "probably a majority of psychiatrists and psychologists." This is a mere sampling of some of the opinion that has been arrayed against too much competition in preteens.

On the other hand, Doctor Creighton J. Hale who is a director of research for Little League Baseball, Inc., expresses quite an opposite opinion. He reviews the available literature on the subject and feels that whatever evidence exists is too contradictory to allow one to come to such a definite conclusion. Obviously, he feels that participation in such competitive pre-adolescent sports as Little League baseball is beneficial. He seems to be correct that there is no definitive research evidence one way or the other and one then must take into account which side of the fence one is standing on as to how the scene looks. Obviously, his opinion would be favorable to competitive sports. The pediatricians, orthopedic surgeons, and psychiatrists who express other opinions may do so from anecdotal observations they have made over the years of clinical cases that come to their attention where they have felt that competitive sports at too early an age has caused some harm. However, this does not make for very conclusive evidence.

In 1962-63, the Research Division of Little League Baseball conducted a very interesting survey of the opinion of thirteen hundred doctors who had sons participating in Little League. One might feel that this is rather a prejudiced sample since the very fact that these doctors are fathers of sons in Little League baseball indicates a belief that this is beneficial or at least not harmful for their boys. Nevertheless, the very favorable opinions cannot be ignored. Many questions were asked but the concluding question was, "Do you believe that playing in Little League baseball was beneficial to your son?" Ninety-four per cent of the doctors felt that it was, including 89 per cent of the psychiatrists who were included in the survey. Even the questions which were directed at the emotional reaction of their children were

answered by the vast bulk of doctors as beneficial. For example, the question, "Did you find that 'playing to win'
produced undesirable responses in your son?" Nine per cent
of the doctors said yes and 91 per cent no. It is interesting
that psychiatrists were even more favorable about this as
4 per cent said yes and 96 per cent said no. One question
where there was some negative reaction was, "Do you think
that Little League baseball is overemphasized?". Twenty per
cent of the doctors said yes, 32 per cent said sometimes and
48 per cent said no. Among the psychiatrists, 16 per cent
said yes, 46 per cent sometimes, and 38 per cent no. About
all one could conclude from this interesting survey is that
doctors whose sons play Little League baseball generally tend
to feel it was beneficial.

The argument against such competitive oriented activities
as Little League baseball or Pop Warner football is that they
put such a high premium on winning on children who are
not psychologically quite ready for this. In an earlier chapter
it was emphasized that at this age the concept of winning is
not so important to a child as it will be during adolescence.
One of the big criticisms of such things as Little League
baseball is its emphasis on tournaments, even national tournaments. The over-glorification of the best teams and best
players would seem not to be too desirable for this age group.
In fact, Little League baseball may encourage "minor leagues"
for those boys who are not quite good enough to make the
regular team in their neighborhood. While on the one hand,
this gives everyone a chance to play that wants to, on the
other hand it tends to emphasize that the best players are the
ones who are the most important.

Many communities run sports leagues for prepubertal children but on a much less competitive basis. For example, in
Ann Arbor, Michigan, several thousand boys play baseball
each summer. However, there is a separate league for each
year of age starting at the age of nine and going through

fifteen and then "a high-school league" after that. Each
team is oriented to the neighborhood and anyone who wants
to play is put on a team. In addition, every member of the
team is supposed to play at least two innings in each game.
No tournaments are held, no victory banquets, and in general there is a downgrading of the only goal of the summer
being to win the league championship. Many other communities have similar arrangements. The big advantage here
over Little League is that all youngsters are the same age
on the team even though there may be considerable variation
in size. In Little League, the children may range in age
from nine through twelve. Some parents have remarked how
frightened their 9-year-old boys became at the prospect of
having to bat against a 12-year-old pitcher. Obviously, this
three years of differential in age at this point makes a tremendous difference in strength and size.

By now, the criticism of parents of children who play in
organized sports has become institutionalized. That is, every-
body knows that the parents are the problem through their
arguing with umpires and demanding victory of their children,
sometimes to the embarrassment of the children. No doubt
there is considerable truth to this, particularly where the
teams are organized on such a basis that the whole goal of
the game is to win rather than to play for the fun of it or
to learn the skills of the game. It may be quite frightening
to the child to realize how much pressure the parents are
putting on him when he might much prefer just to play
for fun. Playing for fun has little place on such teams and
it may result in the less competitive youngsters becoming bored
in self-defense and drifting away from the team before the
season ends.

Another argument used against prepubertal competitive
teams is the possibility of injury. The careful studies by
Hale of injuries among Little League baseball players would
suggest that this is a rather minor issue. Other studies have

revealed that five times as many injuries occur in competitive games than in games which are for fun or practice possibly due to increased tension and pressure on the participants. There are also five times more injuries among junior high school level players than among senior high school age players because of generally poorer coordination and slower reaction time among the younger students. Most of these accidents occur in football as revealed by insurance claims where football may account for one-half to two-thirds of all claims even though football may account for only 10 per cent of the insured activity.

The significance of too much emphasis on winning on adult and especially outstanding competitors is not really known. No doubt many professional or top amateur athletes experience considerable mental stress from their participation but there doesn't seem to be too much worry about them since they are supposedly able to care for themselves. Nevertheless, a most interesting article was written by a psychiatrist, Arnold Beisser, who also was a ranking amateur tennis player. He reflected on many of the famous tennis players he had known and their mental behavior during important matches.

He felt that the intense competition in top competitive tennis allowed acting out of many unconscious conflicts and what would be called "sick" elsewhere was called "color" in sports. It seemed to him that defeating opponents often took on the unconscious meaning of killing the opponent with resulting fear of retaliation. It is particularly important in a sport like tennis where the same top competitors faced each other repeatedly in various tournaments around the world. He noted how some would become too guilty at the specter of defeating (killing) their opponent and would invariably lose the big matches to opponents they could beat in less significant matches. He recalled one champion player who could never allow himself to win by a large margin, even over an easy opponent. Sometimes interesting situations would arise where the player who was losing would become depressed, hang his head in a "suicidal gesture" and begin to miss shots on purpose. The result of this would be to make the aggressor suddenly feel guilty and ease up in his "killing" so that the loser would suddenly begin to improve and sometimes regain the lead. He felt much of the origin of these unconscious implications were related to intense aggressive conflict with the father from early years, particularly because most of the championship players had been taught to play by their fathers. It is interesting to observe the tendency to let up on the victim who is being overwhelmed. This seems to be a reaction that many people show and it is similar to animals. Sometimes when dogs are fighting and one begins to lose, the losing dog will roll over in complete helplessness and the other dog stops the attack. As reflected in our talk about games, the game no longer is fun without a competitor who is trying and so the attack ceases.

The question whether the conditioning aspects of sports are good or harmful is answered primarily in the former. However, the question might be asked as to what the person is being conditioned for. Generally, youngsters are reasonably fit if they are not suffering from frank disease though they may not perform too well on certain specific tests as some of the physical fitness surveys of American youth have demonstrated. If one wishes to increase the performance on these physical fitness tests, then all one has to do is emphasize a program where the muscle groups required for these tests are improved. However, this does not necessarily indicate that the person is more fit than before. It may be unrealistic to expect that a mass program of conditioning will give similar results between people who are very different in their physical needs and capacities. It is questionable whether athletics or physical exercise beyond that normally indulged in by children has any lasting benefits.

With adults, the situation is somewhat different since it is

not the capacity of muscles that is important but the continued vitality of the cardiovascular and respiratory system.
Adequate studies now demonstrate that lack of continued
exercise in middle-aged adults is correlated with higher inci-
dence of serious illness involving these systems. Thus, activities
should be directed towards keeping one's "wind" as good
as possible rather than worrying about the size of the bicep
muscle.

The question as to what one is being kept fit for brings
to mind a most interesting story quoted over the news and
reported in an article about physical fitness: "They say
Africa is a continent of strange contrasts. And Mal Whitfield,
America's two-time Olympic 800-meter champ, certainly
agrees. He learned firsthand on a recent State Department
goodwill tour. Whitfield was supposed to show a group of
natives something about physical training. Mal did a pushup
then asked the group to do likewise. One native after another
tried but no one succeeded. Exasperated, Mal tried a different
exercise. Just then one of the natives leaped over a fence and
disappeared. Whitfield was bugeyed. The fence was a shade
over seven feet high. Then another native raced past him
and into the forest. 'Where's he going?' Whitfield inquired.
'To catch an antelope,' was the answer. Mal shook his head
and walked away muttering to himself, 'And they couldn't do
a pushup.'"

One further note might be added about the general value
of sports particularly for those who are somewhat older. A
study was done by two physicians on ten adult males, age
twenty-three to sixty-five, who were in attendance at a college
football game. Special cardiographic equipment was used
which could remotely record the heart action of these spectators. It was found that all demonstrated marked increase
of heart rate especially with plays which took a long time
to be completed such as punt returns, and other evidence
demonstrated a tendency towards interference with efficient

functioning of the heart muscle. As a result, they raised a question about the risk of being a spectator at sports events for people with chronic cardiac disease. Anyone who has attended many big sporting events has had a number of experiences of seeing someone carried from the stadium on a stretcher and learned later that the individual had died of a heart attack. This seems to be particularly a risk if the spectator has an intense involvement emotionally with one of the teams.

In considering some of the misuses of sports, we will now consider how psychological factors which become transferred from earlier conflict into sports activity can result in athletic injuries. We need to be reminded that we are talking about unconscious processes and not suggesting that athletes are injured purposely within their own knowledge. It might seem unnecessary to make such a comment after the great emphasis on unconscious factors throughout the book. However, a few years ago the author made some comments of a similar nature at a professional meeting and an enterprising sportswriter took the statements out of context to a professional football team to find out how many of them had been hurt on purpose. One can readily imagine the rather salty responses that this sportswriter obtained. We also must keep in context the issue of athletic injuries and recognize that psychological factors alone are not the cause of athletic injuries in all cases but recognize that major emphasis must be placed on proper physical conditioning, protective equipment, and rules of safety.

One might think that in competitive athletics where participation is voluntary that we would not find too much conflict over the aggression in competitive sports. After all, a person knows what he is getting into and only the more successful will compete. We also recognize, however, that some people may be involved in competitive sports for reasons that are not clear to them and we have already considered the possibility of young people being pushed into competitive sports for the sake of their parents' self-esteem before they are old enough for this.

Where there is considerable conflict over display of aggression, the ebb and flow of whether the strength to show the aggression or the fear of it is in dominance may have much to do with the shifting of competitive ability. We even see this in teams and this has much to do with the "upsets" that are so much a part of sports. The team and its individual members give top performance as long as they are willing to be fully aggressive against the opponent. However, if a shift occurs in this balance, perhaps due to some element of luck in the game, the team and its members begin to falter and lose momentum, fearful of being too aggressive, and begin to defend themselves against retaliatory blows. Before, the team had an omnipotent faith in its safety in being aggressive but now old unconscious fears of overwhelming retaliation cause the team to "pull its punches."

We will review two brief case examples where injuries have been effected by this conflict, particularly because the ability to be aggressive or not is so closely related to feelings of manliness and competition with father.

> *Case One:* A young high school boy with little athletic ability but tremendous desire tried out for the baseball team. This boy had been raised somewhat overprotectively with considerable emphasis on the risks in life. As a result, he had grown up to be a not too confident nor particularly aggressive person. Nevertheless, as a compensation, he had entertained phantasies of being an athlete as long as he could remember to prove that he really was able to be manly. His fantasies were never realized, unfortunately, and instead he was the perpetual benchwarmer on any team he tried to join. He was good enough to make the team as a substitute due to tremendous effort but his lack of any real ability prevented

him from being a regular. This particular spring it was apparent to him that, though he had been a substitute on the team the two years preceding, he would probably not make the team at all this year because of a number of more promising newcomers. The boy was a catcher who found himself spending more and more time catching batting practice. Twice that spring he suffered painful bruises on his fingers by failing to keep his right hand closed until the ball was in the mitt. He kept trying until one day in an intrasquad practice game he experienced a severe fracture of his right index finger and the season was over. Rather than being bitterly disappointed, the response of this boy was one of relief as he could now leave the field of manly combat with banners flying high. He had escaped defeat and proof of his weakness through his injury and his splinted finger became a "combat badge" as proof of his aggressive abilities. Obviously the boy did not suffer this injury on purpose and would deny this if it were suggested. Yet, three times in a span of several days he suffered injuries to his fingers which had not occurred to him before and the prevention of which was well known to him.

Case Two: This young man is quite a contrast to the preceding one as he was a much more successful athlete. He was an outstanding high-school football player and track star and had offers of athletic scholarships from several large colleges, finally choosing one at which he enrolled. He started off the sophomore year by making the first string varsity, a rather unusual thing for a sophomore in a university of this size and with such prominent football tradition. Unfortunately, he suffered an injury to his leg and missed the opening game. The injury was not very severe but for reasons not clear to the team physician nor coaches, the leg did not respond to treatment and he continued to hobble through practice sessions. By this time, the other players were gaining momentum and he soon fell out of contention, no longer noticed by the coaches, until he finally dropped from the team. Despite his great successes, this young man had never

CARL A. RUDISILL LIBR
LENOIR RHYNE COLL

felt he achieved sufficient acclaim from his father. His father was a quiet and nondemonstrative man who always seemed to see the gloomy side of life and cautioned the patient against undue optimism. Any demonstration of anger was not encouraged in this family which set a model of passivity and social withdrawal. A younger brother was much more in keeping with the pattern expected of the family, in fact he was rather unsuccessful in athletics and flunked out of college, yet he was the one that seemed to be much more praised by the father. The athletic son finally got the message that the more successfully aggressive he was, the more alien and nonunderstandable he became to his family. While the injury itself may not have been purposeful, it certainly seems that his inability to recover from the injury was purposeful though at an unconscious level. From these two cases we can see how psychological conflict between passivity and aggressivity can be a factor in sports injuries.

A somewhat more subtle solution to conflict over expression of basic urges is the development of what is termed a counterphobic reaction. Because of fear of retaliation for wishes to express aggressive urges when young, the person grows to anticipate with terror some form of body mutilation in the future. As a protection against this, he develops a pattern of "whistling in the dark" by feeling himself totally unafraid and invulnerable to injury. Because deep down he knows this really isn't so, the defense must be turned to repetitively for reassurance. As a result, the person tests and retests himself to prove magically he cannot be seriously hurt by daring and even dangerous activities. Typically, he feels very keyed up for facing danger which is experienced as an exhilirating anticipation. When the danger has been successfully challenged, he feels satisfied and powerful for a short period of time. However, since this is not a real solution, the experience must be repeated. Since this individual is forced into taking so many risks, the law of averages finally catches up with him and he becomes injured and sometimes very seriously. We will describe two examples of this.

Case Three: A young man made his way in this world by performing as a professional motorcycle and auto racer and sometimes as a stunt flyer on the county fair circuit in the Midwest. He had a reputation for foolhardy courage and sometimes had been noted to get quite excited and exhilirated by watching accidents involving other drivers. He, himself, felt exhilirated whenever this occurred to him and he would suffer only minor injuries from which he would return with renewed enthusiasm. His background included the unfortunate fact that his father had been killed in an automobile accident when this man was six weeks old. On the way to the funeral, one of his brothers, his uncle and grandmother were killed in an auto accident. From his earliest memories the patient recalls this gruesome story being retold many times by his mother. In the absence of the father, his oldest brother many years his senior had become a substitute father, a rather harsh one at that. One day this brother and the brother's son were killed in an auto accident and the patient shortly after quit racing and flying. He had to quit because he had become so nervous he could not function behind the wheel after his brother's death. As his symptoms worsened, it was finally necessary for him to enter a psychiatric hospital because of his growing terror at being injured. He experienced repetitive dreams of seeing his brother's mutilated body in the morgue which had been necessary for him to identify.

This man from his earliest years had felt a terrible vulnerability to injury. Certainly his family history would hardly be one to reassure a person about what happens to people who are in automobiles. If such a horrible fate could befall powerful people like his father, a puny figure like himself had little chance. As a result, he anticipated mutilation as a consequence of the most minor expression of aggression. His constant danger defying activities were of a counterphobic type and a magical attempt to undo his vulnerability by constantly conquering danger. This tenuous defense crumbled when his hated older brother was killed, particularly because of the strong feelings of anger he had felt towards his brother for so many years, and he now felt that retaliation must surely follow.

Case Four: This little story unfolded in a hospital emergency suite. An auto accident victim was brought by ambulance and attended by the surgeons. He became such a problem for them to manage that the services of a psychiatrist were required. Although the injuries were painful, they were not life threatening. Nevertheless, the patient was so terrified he was dying that he refused to allow the doctors to give him medical attention. While any accident victim is quite frightened, the usual picture is that of passivity and submission to almost any indignity. The doctors in attendance could not recall having seen a patient whose reaction was so extreme. It was only with great reassurance that it was possible to proceed with the necessary care.

The man's identity soon became quite obvious because of his scarred face and his name which revealed him to be a famous professional hockey star. While the behavior in the accident and the fact that this man is a professional hockey player might seem unrelated, it does suggest something of the nature of counterphobia and how it leads one into danger defying situations. This man made a career out of facing danger and the number of suture scars in his face ran into the hundreds evidencing that he did not always duck in time. For most of us, this would be a risk we would find very difficult to tolerate. For him, however, it was anticipated danger, with the time and place of his own arrangement, so that he had control in a magical sense of his being injured. The accident was something which was quite unplanned for him and his counterphobic mechanism suddenly collapsed revealing a person much more terrified of injury than would be true of most people.

Some people may submit to injuries because of deep uncon-scious feelings of guilt and need for punishment. In fact, these type of people may be unable to allow themselves success when it is so near at hand. It was mentioned earlier in the article by Beisser how many top-ranking players have much diffi-culty with this struggle to win. We will illustrate with an example.

> *Case Five:* A college trackman was one of the top sprinters in the conference. Despite this, in his junior year at the conference championship meet he repeatedly fouled in his specialty and was disqualified. He tried again in his senior year, again had top conference times, but developed a "charley horse" and was urged to rest. Despite strenuous efforts of the coach and trainers to restrain him, he insisted on coming back too soon and developed a severe quadriceps muscle tear and his running career was at an end. This boy had had a very conflicted relationship with his father who was very competitive with the son. Unfortunately, the father had not been very successful and made it clear to the boy that he would not tolerate being made to look bad by his son.

Actively seeking out physical harm may have two mean-ings. Guilt over unacceptable wishes can be expiated by punishment in the form of bodily injury. A more passive and submissive seeking of injury has a somewhat different meaning. A boy who is in terror of mutilation for his ag-gressions allows himself to be hurt or actively seeks to be injured. It is as if he is now saying, "See, I am injured, you do not have to hurt me," or "I am injured and help-less and thus I am no danger to you." We recall how similar this is to the behavior of animals such as dogs who will drive away the overwhelming aggressor by giving up and ruining the game.

It would be quite helpful to people who deal with young-sters in sports situations if certain signs could be found which might lead to the possibility of injury for psychological reasons. A few situations can be suggested:

1. Gross disproportion between athletic ability and willingness to be aggressive. Some boys want to play too badly, want too much to be aggressive, but have so little ability and in their awkwardness may be injured. Other boys have great athletic potential but are afraid to be aggressive and may have to remove themselves from the conflict by injury.

2. Disproportion between father and son as to athletic ability and expression of aggression. Every coach has been plagued by the athletically-successful father who ambitiously pushes his not too capable and not too aggressive son into sports, forcing the boy into competition for which he is not prepared. It may be that for a son to be more capable or more aggressive than his father arouses old terrors over urges long ago to displace the father. An example is a young man of better than average athletic ability who refused to participate in athletics despite his father's urging. His father had been a varsity football player in college and was now a high-ranking business executive. The boy dreamed of athletes who beat him regularly and in college decided to be an English teacher. This was quite unacceptable to his father and thus proved to be a fine method of passive defiance.

3. Lack of adequate control of aggression. The too aggressive athlete who lacks sufficient control over himself may rush blindly into the battle with injury resulting to himself and an opponent. Watching film strips of football injuries has suggested to some observers that certain players develop "tunnel vision" and in their mad charge to make a tackle fail to see blockers who are slightly off the direct line of vision.

4. Fear of injury. The overtimid athlete who hesitates just before being tackled loses his momentum and is more

likely to be injured. If he has such fear of injury, he should confine his sports interest to noncontact sports.

5. History of multiple injuries. As accident proneness can be seen in industrial workers, it also can be seen in sports participants. With a history of multiple injuries, it is only common sense that this person will again suffer injury and the next one may be more serious.

6. Concealment of minor injuries. A frequently voiced complaint by many coaches is that some athletes will attempt to conceal their injuries so that they will not be removed from the game. While this devotion to duty seems commendable, one must wonder whether there is a counterphobic element involved which may leave this person vulnerable to some serious injury, particularly because the present injury may have reduced his coordination and stamina.

7. Exaggerations of injuries. The opposite extreme is the crybaby whose every little bruise requires immediate attention. This constant preoccupation with injuries may indicate that the person is quite frightened of the contact of the game and would better be saved from facing it.

8. Inability to tolerate success. Sometimes an athlete with considerable ability starts out like a worldbeater but then begins to slip and find himself more frequently on the bench. Sometimes this merely represents the young person who was physically mature ahead of his age mates but they have now caught up with him. On the other hand, it may represent his inability to allow himself to continue to be so successful. Injury can be a facesaving way out for this person.

9. Omnipotent feelings of invulnerability. The athlete who seems to relish danger to an unusual degree and displays an omnipotent sense of invulnerability to injury may be demonstrating a counterphobic reaction. This may require him to take increasing and unnecessary risks to prove his vulnerability until finally he faces a serious injury.

The situations listed here may be found among young-sters trying out for any level of competitive teams, whether pre-adolescent teams, or high school, college, or even pro-fessional teams. These boys do not give evidence of psychiatric illness and may seem quite similar to other members of the team except for one or more of the above situations. Never-theless, it would be wise for all who work with athletes to be sensitive to the possibilities that people who fit any of the above categories might have a higher than normal risk of being injured.

In this chapter we have talked about some of the misuses and abuses of sports. Of particular concern has been the overemphasis on winning rather than the more healthly emphasis on participation for all and for fun. Particular concern is expressed about the encouragement of youngsters below the high-school level to participate in overorganized competitive sports which is more for the sake of their parents and coaches than it is for the sake of the boys themselves. It is admitted that there is considerable controversy over this point and no scientific evidence which settles the question in either direction yet this opinion is shared by many who deal with young people. We have also considered how the risk of injury may be much more serious in certain people because of deep psychological experiences they have had earlier in their life and a series of situations are described where this potential might be greater than average. How-ever, no one should be misled to think that the misuses and abuses of sports outweigh the tremendous advantages of sports and recreation participation as discussed in earlier chapters.

REFERENCES

1. Athletic Medical Advisory Committee of the Academy of Medicine of Cincinnati: "I want'a play too!" *Cincinnati Journal of Med-icine, 44*:445-456, 1964.
2. Beisser, Arnold R.: Psychodynamic observations of a sport. *Psycho-analysis and Psychoanalytic Review, 48*:69-76, 1961.

3. Committee on School Health of the American Academy of Pediatrics. Competitive Athletics: a statement of policy. *Pediatrics, 18*:672-675, 1956.

4. Davis, John Eisele: The utilization of play in the construction of healthy mental attitudes. *Mental Hygiene, 20*:49-54, 1936.

5. Hale, Creighton J.: What research says about athletics for pre-high school age children. *Journal of Health-Physical Education-Recreation,* December, 1959.

6. Hale, Creighton J.: Injuries among 771,810 Little League baseball players. *Journal of Sports Medicine and Physical Fitness, 1*:80-83, 1961.

7. Hein, Fred V.: Educational aspects of athletics for children. *Journal of the American Medical Association, 168*:1434-1438, 1958.

8. Hoxie, Jean.: Competitive athletics for children. *Journal of the American Medical Association, 168*:1439-1440, 1958.

9. Maksim, George: Desirable athletics for children. *Journal of the American Medical Association, 168*:1431-1433, 1958.

10. McCammon, Robert W., and Sexton, Alan W.: Implications of longitudinal research in fitness programs. *Journal of the American Medical Association, 168*:1440-1445, 1958.

11. McGuigan, R. A.: Athletics and the child. *Archives of Pediatrics, 78*:43-47, 1961.

12. Reichert, J. L. Competitive athletics for pre-teen-age children: a challenge to physicians. *Journal of the American Medical Association, 166*:1701-1707, 1958.

13. Research Division, Little League Baseball, Inc. 1,300 doctors evaluate Little League Baseball, 1962-63.

14. Rose, Kenneth D., and Dunn, F. Lowell: The heart of the spectator sportsman. *Medical Times, 92*:945-951, 1964.

15. Shaffer, Thomas E. Are Little Leagues good for children? *Pennsylvania Medical Journal, 59*:447-450, 1956.

16. Simmons, James E.: Prevention and treatment of the undue emotional aspects of athletic competition. *Journal of the Indiana Medical Association, 52*:1763-1765, 1959.

INDEX

[111]